# Praise for *Therapeutic Yoga for Trauma Recovery*

"Arielle masterfully bridges her well-developed model of therapeutic yoga with polyvagal theory. In doing so, she has creatively found paths to support the recovery of her readers as they share, through the powerful and insightful tools embedded in yoga, a journey of re-embodiment, co-regulation, healing, and discovery."

> —**Stephen W. Porges, PhD,** distinguished university scientist and founding director of the Traumatic Stress Research Consortium, Kinsey Institute, Indiana University Bloomington; professor of psychiatry, University of North Carolina at Chapel Hill

"In *Therapeutic Yoga for Trauma Recovery*, Dr. Arielle Schwartz blends the insights learned through modern science with the intuitive, ancient wisdom of traditional practices. As an acupuncturist and yoga teacher trainer, I have witnessed yoga practice be transformative for thousands of students, teachers, and clinicians alike. I am deeply grateful to Dr. Schwartz for so beautifully articulating the importance, versatility, and meaning of yoga practices in healing, and for showing us how to anchor these practices in compassion and sustainable growth."

> —**Tiffany Cruikshank, LAc, MAOM, E-RYT,** founder of Yoga Medicine®

"This excellent resource on trauma therapeutics fits well as a training text for schools or a personal journal and activity roadmap to wellness. It is scholarly, science-backed, and packed with apt definitions of our current understanding of neuropsychology. But what I love most about Arielle's way of addressing trauma is that she doesn't see the process as grim, but as an inviting, warm, and curious adventure that we undertake with every part of our humanness. She cleverly reframes classic movement and breath and offers new somatic/embodiment work. Arielle eliminates any rigidity around looking within, so even meditation seems more approachable. This is clearly a labor of love, and applying the wisdom of this book gives us a glimpse of *smarana*, remembering who we are."

> —**Beth Spindler, C-IAYT, E-RYT 500,** yoga therapist, teacher, and author of *Yoga Therapy for Fear: Treating Anxiety, Depression and Rage with the Vagus Nerve and Other Techniques*

"Trauma: a tale as old as human life on this planet. Over thousands of years, many powerful healing modalities have emerged to guide people back to an experience of wholeness. *Therapeutic Yoga for Trauma Recovery* brilliantly illuminates these modalities by weaving together major systems of trauma recovery: yoga, embodiment, and polyvagal theory. Dr. Schwartz offers an empowering holistic guide to reclaiming your deepest sense of belonging: to yourself, to others, and the world around you. I highly recommend this book for those currently on their personal journey, as well as anyone working as a practitioner."

—**Scott Lyons, PhD, RYT-500,** founder of The Embody Lab

"The science of self-care has grown by leaps and bounds over the past few decades. We now know that regular self-care practices offer an essential tool to navigate the inevitable ups and downs of life on planet earth. With her new book, Dr. Arielle Schwartz has created an incredible resource for how we can integrate the important findings from polyvagal theory with ancient yogic breath, movement, and awareness practices. The result is a must-have guide to the numerous techniques yoga offers for fostering greater well-being and balance in life."

—**Eva Norlyk Smith, PhD,** president, YogaUOnline.com

"In her newest book, Arielle's expert voice invites us into the sacred space of self, knowingness, and healing with the authentic poignance of one who has traveled the journey themselves. It is with loving kindness and compassionate wisdom that she invites us to experience new opportunities for healing through connecting inward using powerful and valuable tools that will transform your relationship with your body and, ultimately, with yourself."

—**Kate Truitt, PhD, MA, MBA,** CEO of the Trauma Counseling Center and Havening Techniques® global director of research and curriculum development

"In *Therapeutic Yoga for Trauma Recovery*, Dr. Arielle Schwartz combines her extensive background and experience working with trauma survivors with a warm and welcoming style. The book covers a lot of ground, addressing the needs of yoga teachers, students, and therapists when working with a trauma-informed approach to yoga practice. I was particularly impressed with the practical therapeutic guidelines in the appendix for individual yoga therapy sessions and for a six-week therapeutic class, where she recommends specific movement and breathing exercises from the text."

—**Joann Lutz, MSW, LICSW, C-IAYT, E-RYT,** author of *Trauma Healing in the Yoga Zone: A Guide for Mental Health Professionals, Yoga Therapists, and Yoga Teachers*

"Embodiment practices and the health of the nervous system are key components of contemporary psychology and physical well-being. Dr. Arielle Schwartz does it all well. In this book, she is a brilliant cartographer of the nervous system and she shows us, through her deft integration of ancient yoga practices and contemporary polyvagal theory, that choice and safety can be cultivated through embodied breath, conscious movement, and stillness. There are many wise clinical pearls embedded in this book that I regularly use with my patients to soothe trauma imprints, which so often show up as neurologic patterns such as cognitive decline or chronic illness. One of the root causes of trauma is disconnection, and Arielle shows us how to reconnect with ourselves and with each other, even more so if you have the opportunity to practice trauma-informed yoga with her. How fortunate we all are that Arielle shares her highly evolved mastery with us in this jewel of a book as a path to waking up and healing the nervous system of the world."

—**Ilene Naomi Rusk, PhD,** clinical psychologist, neuropsychologist, and director of the Healthy Brain Program at the Brain and Behavior Clinic

"As a medical physician addressing the effects of stored trauma on our biology, I consider this book a must read for all professionals who work with people who have a human body. This is not just for trauma, though it will be a game-changer for those who have trauma patterns. By applying polyvagal theory to embodiment yoga in her wonderful and unique way, Arielle has just set a new standard for working with the body and a chronic freeze response."

—**Aimie Apigian, MD, MS, MPH**

"*Therapeutic Yoga for Trauma Recovery* is a magnificently written new book by Arielle Schwartz. You will be empowered to understand your nervous system and the vagus nerve as never before. Dr. Schwartz's expertise and compassion shine through each chapter. You can count on her as a reliable guide on your healing journey. This book will take you on a deeper dive into yoga as a path for recovery. I highly recommend it!"

—**Joanne Spence, BSW, MA, E-RYT 500, C-IAYT,** author of
*Trauma-Informed Yoga: A Toolbox for Therapists*

"Arielle's teachings weave together deeply embodied knowledge, accessibility, and heart. The tools she offers provide a pathway toward hope in these incredibly trying times. Arielle has a way of connecting that is clear, compassionate, and impactful. Her work has never been needed more, and I am looking forward to sharing this offering with my students. What I know is this: When we use the tools offered to us in Arielle's book, we have the ability to not only heal ourselves, but to heal the world."

—**Lauren Lewis,** mother, yoga teacher, chef, and student

"A treasure for any somatic psychotherapist and seeker of trauma healing alike. Dr. Schwartz elegantly guides the self-discovery process through integrating two powerful healing systems. The practical application of yoga, the ancient body wisdom practice, with the contemporary neurophysiological model of trauma recovery is an effective offering. This trauma-informed lens empowers the inner healer that is both gentle and transformative. These precise and accessible practices will benefit trauma well-being and enhance any clinician's skill set that values somatic therapies."

—**Manuela Mischke-Reeds, LMFT,** author of *Somatic Psychotherapy Toolbox*, director of Hakomi Institute of California, and founder of Innate Somatic Intelligence Trauma Therapy Approaches

"In her newest book, reflective of a lifelong journey, Dr. Arielle Schwartz brings forth a brilliant synthesis of the bodies of wisdom that have illuminated her path of healing. She guides readers through a journey toward embodied healing that is rooted in compassion, curiosity, and care. Through her gift for writing, Arielle offers a wise, deeply human, and heart-centered perspective that empowers the reader to be with the inherently multifaceted experience of being alive. As a collective, we are being called to remember our shared humanity. As we reorient to this new path, Arielle's book is a wise and warm ally helping to light the way."

—**Amy Annesley, LCSW, EMDR CIT**

# Therapeutic

# YOGA

## for
# Trauma
# Recovery

Applying the Principles of Polyvagal Theory
for Self-Discovery, Embodied Healing,
and Meaningful Change

## Arielle Schwartz, PhD, CCTP-II, E-RYT

With forewords by
Stephen W. Porges, PhD
Tiffany Cruikshank, LAc, MAOM, E-RYT

Published by
PESI Publishing, Inc.
3839 White Ave
Eau Claire, WI 54703

Cover: Amy Rubenzer
Editing: Jenessa Jackson, PhD
Layout: Amy Rubenzer & Gretchen Panzer

ISBN: 9781683735052 (print)
ISBN: 9781683735069 (ePUB)
ISBN: 9781683735076 (ePDF)

PESI Publishing
pesipublishing.com

# Dedication

*In gratitude to the teachers who have illuminated a path of the heart. I will forever be a student.*

*In dedication to my students, who trust me to be your guide. You have inspired this book.*

*Together, we courageously shine our light into the darkness to make this world a brighter place.*

# About the Author

 **Arielle Schwartz,** PhD, CCTP-II, E-RYT, is a licensed clinical psychologist, certified complex trauma professional, and experienced registered yoga teacher with a private practice in Boulder, Colorado. As an internationally sought-out teacher, EMDR therapist, somatic practitioner, and leading voice in the healing of PTSD and complex trauma, she is the author of six books, including *The Complex PTSD Workbook*, *The Complex PTSD Treatment Manual*, and *The Post-Traumatic Growth Guidebook*. Learn more about Arielle at www.drarielleschwartz.com.

# Table of Contents

# Foreword

## Stephen W. Porges, PhD

Distinguished University Scientist
Founding Director, Traumatic Stress Research Consortium
Kinsey Institute
Indiana University Bloomington

Professor of Psychiatry
University of North Carolina at Chapel Hill

I have had the good fortune to be involved in an ongoing, engaging dialogue with Arielle on how several of the principles embedded in polyvagal theory are related to yoga. In writing the foreword to this book, in which Arielle masterfully bridges her well-developed model of therapeutic yoga with polyvagal theory, I now have an opportunity to welcome you, her readers, into our dialogue. (I expect those of you who are therapists are more likely to be interested in this discussion. For those of you who are new to polyvagal theory—or to yoga—I assure you that Arielle's book makes for a wonderful introduction.)

For me, it is humbling to contrast my work on polyvagal theory with yoga. Yoga is a thoughtful, well-developed system designed to optimize mind and body that has evolved over thousands of years, whereas polyvagal theory was initially conceptualized in 1994 and is still emerging. This book is organized by introducing the eight limbs, or *sutras*, of yoga that were detailed by Patañjali over 2,000 years ago. These include, as Arielle explains, "ethical principles, physical postures, conscious breathing, and meditation practices that focus your attention on the healing power of the present moment."

As you can see in the following table, the eight limbs can be described by a collection of aphorisms that encompass much of human experience. Similar to polyvagal theory, there is an implicit hierarchy in the limbs. Through practice, the student of yoga moves through the limbs. From a polyvagal perspective, this progression leads to personal transformations dependent on the focus of the practice.

| Sutra | Practice and Process | Functional Experience |
|-------|---------------------|----------------------|
| Yamas | Cultural/moral restraints | How we relate to others |
| Niyamas | Self-awareness | How we relate to ourselves |
| Asana | Posture | How we relate to our body |
| Pranayama | Breath | How we relate to our breath |
| Pratyahara | Sensory withdrawal | How we relate to our sense organs |
| Dharana | Concentration | How we relate to our mind |
| Dhyana | Meditation | Moving beyond the mind |
| Samadhi | Meditative absorption | Deep realization and inner union |

Initially, the practitioner transitions from external factors to bodily processes linked to the regulation of the autonomic nervous system, then to sensory and mental processes that challenge their autonomic state, and finally to explorations of an expanded consciousness. Although the latter is not specifically within the realm of polyvagal theory, hypothetically the mental processes that include the exploration of consciousness involve higher cortical structures. Consistent with polyvagal theory, these processes, including creativity and spirituality, require that the individual be in a safe context and in a calm physiological state managed by the social engagement system and ventral vagal pathways.

The hierarchy of the eight limbs can be deconstructed into four principles based on polyvagal theory:

- First, the nervous system must cope with and adapt to the challenges of the external world, which at times may be broadcasting cues of threat. This is done through dynamic adjustments of autonomic state to support movement by ventral vagal withdrawal and sympathetic excitation and, when necessary, to downregulate this metabolically costly strategy to conserve resources by immobilizing and, at times, feigning death via dorsal vagal pathways.

- Second, before we can attempt to optimize our mental and physiological function, we need to be aware of our own body. This process is called *interoception*. It is assumed that as our interoceptive skills improve, the feedback loops that govern our physiology will enhance the regulation of our organs and support the homeostatic functions of health growth and restoration.

- Third, the use of posture and breath provide systematic changes that function as neural exercises that promote the regulation of our organs and are tangible skills to optimize the neural regulation of bodily organs to support homeostatic functions.

- Fourth, sensory challenges and mental effort provide top-down neural exercises that regulate visceral organs and create a neural platform to explore consciousness.

We can see many parallels between the constructs of polyvagal theory and the systems described in yoga, as I explored as a coauthor in an earlier publication (Sullivan et al., 2018). In fact, I was surprised by how many parallels we found between yoga, an ancient model of human anatomy and function, and polyvagal theory, a contemporary neuroscience model. Thus, polyvagal theory offers a functional neurophysiological lexicon for yoga, giving a contemporary scientific voice to the ancient wisdom embedded in yoga practices. Polyvagal theory could help more therapists to recognize that yoga is a neurophysiologically based path to healing—one that addresses physiological imbalances with easily accessible practices that allow us to more accurately sense the body, more appropriately breathe, more efficiently move, and more effectively rest in states of stillness without being hypervigilant for cues of threat.

In developing polyvagal theory, I was not focused on deconstructing yoga. However, I was intellectually curious about the overlap between the structures involved in each. In particular, I conceptualized pranayama yoga—often called the yoga of breath—as a yoga of the social engagement system. In the realm of polyvagal theory, the function of the calming ventral cardioinhibitory vagal pathways is optimized during slow exhalations and further potentiated during abdominal breathing. The neurophysiology of this system has been known for more than 100 years. In fact, the historic physiologist H. E. Hering (1910) identified cardioinhibitory vagal fibers using respiratory rhythms, paving the way for other researchers to document cardiac vagal tone through its functional impact on beat-to-beat heart rate (e.g., respiratory sinus arrhythmia). Polyvagal theory has further delineated the construct of vagal tone by emphasizing that in humans and other social mammals, the primary cardioinhibitory vagal fibers travel through a pathway originating in an area of the brainstem known as the ventral vagal complex. Thus, slow exhalations, especially those involving movement of the diaphragm, have a powerful calming effect by recruiting vagal pathways.

The social engagement system, which I conceptualized in 1998, is functionally the target system through which pranayama yoga works. It is the system linking breath, facial muscles, and vocalization to the vagal cardioinhibitory pathways that calm the body. The social engagement system is a product of a repurposed autonomic nervous system that emerged during the phylogenetic transition from asocial reptiles to social mammals. The repurposed nervous system resulted in a brainstem area—the ventral vagal complex—which integrated the regulation of the striated muscles of the face and head, via special visceral efferent pathways, with the regulation of a ventral vagal cardioinhibitory pathway. The result of this functional interaction was a bidirectional system that conveys our autonomic state in both facial expression and intonation of vocalizations, and that also provides a portal to manipulate our autonomic state through the motoric actions of facial expression, vocalization, and listening. Yes, even listening, since changes in neural tone to the middle ear muscles influence our ability to detect low frequency predator sounds and enhance the extraction of meaning from voice.

As polyvagal theory became embedded in clinical strategies to treat survivors of trauma, my interest in pranayama yoga—and its overlap with the social engagement system—was renewed. I realized the practices that collectively define pranayama yoga represent a sophisticated strategy of neural exercises of the social engagement system. These yoga practices are based on remarkable insights into a neurophysiology that links the sensory and motor systems of the muscles of the face and head with the ventral vagal regulation of our heart and bronchi. Thus, pranayama yoga should be regarded as a technique of neuromodulation with long-term health benefits.

The profound impact of trauma is frequently imprinted on the actions of the social engagement system. In the field of trauma-informed therapeutic yoga, it is the social engagement system that broadcasts the physiological state of the client and provides powerful portals for therapeutic forms of yoga to support their healing. In polyvagal terms, trauma retunes the autonomic nervous system from supporting sociality and co-regulation to supporting defenses. This transition shifts the nervous system from being interpersonally accessible to being vigilant of threat. In individuals with a severe trauma history, the social engagement system has effectively been turned off to optimize threat reactions, which is reflected in flat, unexpressive faces; lack of intonation in their voices; and difficulties in being touched or feeling safe in proximity to others. Underlying the expressed features of a downregulated social engagement system is an autonomic nervous system in a state of defense.

From a contemporary neuroscience perspective, yoga practices anticipated by millennia how movement and breath can be structured into neural exercises that rehabilitate and optimize the neural functioning of the autonomic nervous system. In my own area of research, I have been in awe of the deep understanding of neuroanatomy that is embedded in ancient yoga practices. For me, this is highlighted in pranayama yoga and its implicit understanding of the structures that form the social engagement system, a system that I struggled to conceptualize only a few decades ago. In addition, the yoga postures (asana) are effective neural exercises that challenge blood pressure regulation and that, at times, stimulate afferents to the autonomic nervous system via sacral and cranial nerves.

Polyvagal theory functions like a Rosetta stone, decoding the wisdom of the ancient yoga traditions through our current scientific understanding. By integrating the principles of polyvagal theory into therapeutic yoga, Arielle has creatively found paths to support the recovery of her clients and students as they share, through the powerful and insightful tools embedded in yoga, a journey of re-embodiment, co-regulation, healing, and discovery. I look forward to the future dialogues we will have exploring these paths.

## References

Hering, H. E. (1910). A functional test of heart vagi in man. *Münchener Medizinische Wochenschrift*, *57*(2), 1930–1932.

Porges, S. W. (1998). Love: An emergent property of the mammalian autonomic nervous system. *Psychoneuroendocrinology*, *23*(8), 837–861. https://doi.org/10.1016/s0306-4530(98)00057-2

Sullivan, M. B., Erb, M., Schmalzl, L., Moonaz, S., Noggle Taylor, J., & Porges, S. W. (2018). Yoga therapy and polyvagal theory: The convergence of traditional wisdom and contemporary neuroscience for self-regulation and resilience. *Frontiers in Human Neuroscience*, 67. https://doi.org/10.3389/fnhum.2018.00067

# Foreword

## Tiffany Cruikshank, LAc, MAOM, E-RYT

Founder of Yoga Medicine®

When people think about yoga, often the first image that comes to mind is of the meditative monk, high on a hill, in silent and solitary contemplation. But in contrast to this image of stillness, even while in the most seemingly static pose, yoga can also be highly dynamic. Yoga teaches us to greet our bodies where they are and enter into a lifelong conversation that helps us more flexibly experience the world around us and within us.

If we have put too much stock in the silent, meditative yogi model, we may tend to demonize the "fight-or-flight" sympathetic nervous system and idealize the "rest-and-digest" parasympathetic system with a simplistic view: "Stress is bad, rest is good." But the more complex truth is that our brilliant nervous system is a partnership, a powerful kinship that is essential to our human experience. Neither the sympathetic nor the parasympathetic nervous system can be permitted to dominate the other, or we will cut off our access to large parts of our potential to live fully in this world.

In *Therapeutic Yoga for Trauma Recovery*, Dr. Arielle Schwartz has perfectly captured this lifelong collaboration, blending the insights learned through modern science with the intuitive, ancient wisdom of traditional practices. The science she shares explains to our rational brains what our bodies have known all along: Yoga helps us integrate all facets of our experience, simultaneously grounding us and energizing us, guiding us through our experience of the present moment as a form of preventative medicine. At the root of yoga's power to heal is its education of a flexible nervous system, one in which improved vagal tone helps respectfully balance the intricate facets of our nervous system. It is this dynamic, continuous exchange of energy that grants us full access to our wide-awake experience of the world, without hypervigilance, excessive fear, numbing, or other maladaptive responses we may have developed to cope with our trauma.

An important component of this approach is the fascia, the fabric of the nervous system and a major intervention point with yoga. The fascia is considered our largest sensory organ, a living matrix woven throughout the body that helps influence and regulate our nervous system flexibility. By consciously learning how fascial work intersects with polyvagal science, we can grant ourselves greater understanding, cultivate self-compassion, and encourage ourselves to move toward healing. As yoga helps us dynamically address and release the "issues in our tissues," we learn their lessons and continuously improve our vagal tone, allowing us to meet day-to-day and year-to-year challenges with greater openness, confidence, and spontaneous flexibility.

Dr. Schwartz beautifully articulates how yoga can empower us to blend this curiosity and compassion with a modern understanding of our nervous system. Unlike the traditional gas pedal (SNS) vs. brake (PNS) model, her more holistic description helps us understand the importance of nuances and moving parts, the different aspects and purposes of a flexible nervous system. This awareness helps us better support our own individual needs and heal from long-standing trauma, recognizing that this work is both the means and the end of a dynamic, ever-deepening practice.

As an acupuncturist and yoga teacher trainer, I have witnessed yoga practice be transformative for thousands of students, teachers, and clinicians alike. I have used yoga's simple, accessible self-care tools to help people from all walks of life to embody these complex physiological principles, enabling them to learn to draw wisdom from their trauma experiences, recover their health, create depth and meaning, and truly appreciate their lives. I am deeply grateful to Dr. Schwartz for so beautifully articulating the importance, versatility, and meaning of yoga practices in healing, and for showing us how to anchor these practices in compassion and sustainable growth.

# Acknowledgments

Teachers come in many forms: in the formality of a classroom, the wisdom of a beloved book, and the spontaneity of synchronistic meetings with strangers. For me, the most influential yoga teachers have been my family and closest friends. At least once a year, my mother tells me the story about her pregnancy with me. She shares how she escaped the summer heat by floating in the Long Island Sound—how she felt completely at peace when carried by the gentle currents that ebbed and flowed from the sea. I have a sense of how these rhythmic pulsations were woven into the nourishment of her heartbeat and breath that surrounded me. While life outside of the womb has grown increasingly complicated, I can still access this gift of spacious grace. Carolyn Schwartz, I consider you my first yoga teacher and am so very grateful to give this gift back to you. Thank you for continuing to practice with me; I cherish each moment of breathing and moving together.

My second yoga teacher was my stepfather, Victor Goldman, who came into my life when I was four. You playfully guided my third-grade class to roar like lions, hiss like snakes, find our roots, and reach our branches toward the sun. These playful memories provide the foundation for how I teach yoga today. Your kind heart and unconditional love have helped me in immeasurable ways.

Thank you also to my children, Eliana and Ian. When I became a mother, I felt the powerful sense of responsibility that comes with knowing that my actions directly influence the ease of embodiment for another person. I remember anxiously paging through a stack of books on my bedside table, each offering advice for how to best nurture my children. I also recall the day that I realized that my answers would not be found in a book. This was when I learned to trust my intrinsic wisdom. Thank you from the depths of my heart.

I am also deeply grateful to my husband, Bruce. We met through our mutual love of movement, and our journey together as partners and parents has supported me to grow and expand my wings to see horizons beyond my wildest dreams. Thank you for your steadiness.

Thank you to Dr. Betty Cannon for your wise and guiding presence in my life, both personally and professionally. I am also deeply grateful to Dr. Scott Lyons and the Embody Lab team for the vision and support of my applied polyvagal theory in yoga course. I am indebted to Randall Redfield for the warmest invitation to join the Polyvagal Institute family. And to Dr. Stephen Porges, I am grateful for your kindness and availability for collaboration as I integrate your pioneering work into the practice of yoga.

Once again, I have had the honor of working with the attentive and skillful team at PESI Publishing. Karsyn Morse, I am grateful for the caring and collaborative team you have created. Kate Sample, thank you for hearing my vision and supporting me with this book from start to finish. Jenessa Jackson, I feel honored to have you as my editor. You are gifted in your ability to smooth out my rough edges and refine the finished product.

When creating this book, I knew that I wanted to collaborate with a photographer who could help convey the feeling of the practices to help guide my readers. Jessica Kimak, thank you for listening to my vision. I am grateful for your attention to detail and the care you took in developing just the right images that bring this book to life.

I am so deeply appreciative of my friends, who inspire me with their open hearts and their willingness to be of service in a complicated world. Thank you to Katie Hayden-Lewis for accompanying me on this journey for the last thirty years. I am so grateful for our laughter and shared reverence for the sacred. Pritham Kaur Khalsa, while you no longer are alive to receive this message, I will never forget you and the day you took me to the pivotal yoga class in college that helped realign my life.

Thank you to Robin Hubbard for listening to my heart and leaning in when I need a friend. Thank you to Yashoda Devi Ma for helping me learn the art of stillness through meditation. I am appreciative of Joann Lutz for your willingness to read through the draft of this book and provide me with valuable feedback that helped clarify this material. Thank you to Barb Maiberger for recognizing that my "book about yoga" was ready to be born.

Finally, I am so very grateful for the web of connection and support I experience with all of you: Marcella Moy, Linda Baird, Shyama Creavan, Ilene Naomi Rusk, Becky Degrossa, Deb Azorsky, Abi Lee, Karen Thorson, Laura Underhill, Debra Baskett, Donna Roe Daniell, Angela Grace, Sally Bowman, Amy Annesley, Seneca Murley, Robin Memel-Fox, Joy Traxler, Galina Ivanova Denzel, Raj Seymour, Lauren Lewis, and Bonnie Pierce.

# Preface

I was first introduced to yoga in 1979, when I was seven years old, while taking family vacations to ashrams in rural Pennsylvania and upstate New York. I carry two distinct memories from those trips. The first memory involves sitting in the children's room, where I learned about a light that lives inside of each of us, and I felt a sense of warmth and ease settle in my body. The second memory is attending an evening ritual in a large, dimly lit hall that was filled with the sounds of people chanting and the scent of incense burning. One by one, people filed toward the front of the room to receive *shaktipat*, which is a kind of transmission of energy where the guru uses their inner light to ignite or wake up another person's inner light. I walked to the front of the room with my mother and stepfather until we reached Swami Muktananda, who touched the tops of our heads with a peacock feather. The next day we traveled back home. Within a few weeks, our house caught on fire, destroying everything inside. My mother and stepfather had an eerie feeling that the shaktipat had ignited more than our inner light.

At the time of the fire, I was staying at my father's house, as my parents had gone through a conflictual divorce when I was four years old. My early memories of their fights are accompanied by vague sensory memories of feeling afraid and lonely. From that point forward, my life was defined by the rhythm of traveling back and forth between their markedly different households. I felt most at home with my mother and stepfather, who were both psychotherapists and encouraged the open expression of emotions. In contrast, I felt uncomfortable and unsettled with my father and stepmother, who emphasized learning and knowledge but were quick to dismiss or ignore my emotions. Whenever I stayed with them, unexpressed emotions of anger, jealousy, and grief built up within me and weighed down my young body.

My mother told me about the fire over the phone. I was afraid and sad, but I pretended I was okay—a pseudo-strength that was reinforced in my father's house—as I sensed that they couldn't handle my grief. Between the divorce and the fire, I had experienced two substantial disruptions to my sense of safety in the world before my eighth birthday. As a result, I still carry within me a visceral knowing of groundlessness.

My experiences of yoga offered me a sense of freedom and playfulness that served as powerful antidotes to the losses that dominated my early life. While I was in the third grade, my stepfather came to my school every Friday and taught yoga to my whole class. We pretended to be cobras, camels, cats, and cows. We made funny sounds and laughed. My imagination helped me transcend the desks, books, numbers, and maps that filled the classroom. I could temporarily forget about being uprooted from my soot-filled home. I had a respite from my worries. I was a tree with roots that extended deep into the earth and branches that reached up into the sky. I was a ferocious lion who could roar courageously. I was the crescent moon shining my light for all to see.

As I grew older, the yoga classes that carried me through that pivotal year faded into the past. I felt increasingly uncomfortable and awkward for reasons I could not yet understand. Only years later did I realize that I was shrouded in shame from my childhood wounds, and it nearly swallowed me whole. These feelings of shame and unworthiness emerged as anxiety and panic by the time I went to college. I chronically felt as though I didn't belong, so in order to survive, I dissociated. I became as small as possible. I compressed my light and learned how to hide. I masked my pain with a well-developed capacity to pretend that I was okay—even though deep inside I felt as if I was dying.

I continued to cut myself off from my emotions until my senior year of college, when a friend of mine invited me to attend a yoga class. Breathing and moving my body brought me back to a familiar ground. Within a year, I committed myself to a daily practice and began therapy. With the compassionate guidance of caring yoga teachers and psychotherapists, I learned to trust my own capacity to ride emotional waves as they arose on and off the yoga mat. I accepted that allowing another person to see my pain was essential to my healing journey. I concluded that while we cannot change what happened in the past, living in the here and now empowers us to shape the future.

Out of a longing to understand more about the body-mind relationship, I pursued my yoga teacher training, a master's degree in somatic psychology, and a subsequent doctoral degree in clinical psychology. I have since dedicated my practice to the treatment of post-traumatic stress through the development of an integrative mind-body treatment model that includes somatic psychology, eye movement desensitization and reprocessing (EMDR) therapy, mindfulness, and therapeutic yoga.

In 2012, I had my first meeting with Dr. Stephen Porges, whose polyvagal theory has radically transformed trauma-informed care. His work provides a compassionate way of understanding the symptoms of post-traumatic stress from a physiological perspective and helps us recognize why breathing, movement, and nourishing social connections are all key elements to the healing process. Indeed, these are the same factors that my yoga students have told me are most beneficial about our classes. They need safe social interactions as much as the yoga practices themselves in order to heal. I began partnering with Dr. Porges to teach applied polyvagal theory in yoga, which planted the seeds for this book.

In this book, I offer you the yogic philosophy and practices that consistently bring me home to myself. It is my greatest hope that these pages will help you connect to the wisdom that resides within your body, mind, and spiritual heart. May this guided journey support you to cultivate a reliable felt sense of ease and equanimity that radiates from your inner light out to the world.

# Introduction

The human experience is a profound journey that encompasses joy and pain, love and loss. Although times of stress are inevitable in our complex world, many of us will also face at least one traumatic event in the course of our lifetime. Trauma, by definition, refers to any frightening, shocking, or life-threatening event that overwhelms your capacity to physically cope with or emotionally process your experience. It can involve a single, isolated incident or, in the case of complex trauma, it can reflect the accumulation of repeated, chronic events. For some, these wounds begin in childhood in the form of abuse or neglect. For many, this personal suffering is compounded by the collective trauma that results from pandemics, climate change, or systemic racism.

When you have experienced trauma in any form, it can impair your sense of belonging. It can cause you to lose faith in the trustworthiness of others or to feel betrayed by your family, community, or country. In some cases, it can lead to a loss of identity or a spiritual crisis. You might question whether there is goodness in this world. Many of us also carry legacy wounds of unhealed trauma from previous generations, which are passed down in the form of emotional and physical tension. These hidden wounds can lead to a higher sensitivity to anxiety or depression, greater susceptibility for post-traumatic stress disorder (PTSD), and medically unexplained chronic pain or illness. You may end up feeling disconnected from your body and lose the capacity to feel fully alive.

Not only can trauma disconnect you from your body, but it can also leave you feeling uprooted from the ground you walk upon. You may feel flooded by intrusive sensations or emotions, become hypervigilant to your surroundings, and avoid people or places that remind you of the traumatic experience. You might feel keyed up with anxiety and panic, want to shut down with fatigue and depression, or alternate between these high and low arousal symptoms. You might also not have a clear memory of the traumatic event, either because it occurred at a very young age or because traumatic stress is interfering with your capacity to recall images. However, your body might still carry the burdens of the trauma in the form of tension, chronic pain, or illness. If your traumatic experiences began in childhood, you are also likely to experience shame, which can interfere with your sense of self and your ability to make meaningful relationships with others.

Healing from trauma asks you to develop the capacity to turn toward your suffering without over-identifying with your wounds. Traditional treatment approaches chart a path to healing by asking you to recount the narrative of the specific event or loss. However, since trauma symptoms are as much physical as they are psychological, interventions that focus on telling the story of the distressing event are often insufficient to help you fully heal. Moreover, interventions that focus on rapid exposure to disturbing memories or feelings states can be retraumatizing or harmful.

Given that the physical symptoms of PTSD reflect an imbalance in the autonomic nervous system, which is your body's stress response system, healing from trauma also requires interventions that restore your nervous system to a state of stability, allowing you to sleep well, relax, and digest. Yoga is one such path to healing, offering you the tools to address these physiological imbalances through practices that allow you to sense your body, change how you breathe, move stuck energy with movement, and rest into stillness. This allows you to heal without relying upon a story or narrative about the events of your past. Yoga practices help you build your somatic resources, which allow you to feel empowered, strong, grounded, clearheaded, inspired, spacious, relaxed, and at ease. In doing so, you broaden your capacity to turn toward your distress while simultaneously remaining connected to your resources and strengths.

At its core, therapeutic yoga bridges a path of healing between the psyche and the body. The word *psyche* comes from ancient Greece and is often translated as "the soul," our undying and immortal essence. The word *yoga* comes from Sanskrit and is translated as "to yoke, join, or unite" the body, mind, breath, and soul. Therapeutic yoga brings together these two wisdoms as a way to help you grow in the face of adverse or challenging life events. The path of yoga not only includes physical postures, conscious breathing, and mindfulness, but it also offers a spiritual perspective that can help you recognize that your traumatic events can be catalysts for growth. This does not mean that traumatic events happened for a reason; rather, you have within you the capacity to derive a sense of meaning out of your suffering. You commit yourself to the sacred task of attending to your pain, despair, and grief until you recognize that you can create a meaningful future.

## What to Expect in This Book

This book walks you through the sacred path of yoga to facilitate your own courageous journey of self-discovery that will help you release the adverse effects of trauma from your body and mind. If you are a therapist or yoga teacher, you will learn how to guide your clients or students through these practices. While yoga is frequently sought out by students to help with trauma recovery, not all teachers are trauma-informed and, as a result, they might not know how to respond to students who are struggling with physical pain or emotional distress in class. On the other hand, many therapists are trained to treat trauma but do not know how to integrate yogic principles and practices into their work with clients. This book helps bridge that gap.

Through the lens of interpersonal biology, polyvagal theory, and somatic psychology, you will explore the physiological underpinnings of how stressful or traumatic events take their toll on your mind and body. You will be invited to become a compassionate witness to your mind, explore conscious breathing, and discover mindful movement practices that enhance your mental, emotional, and physical health. Although traditional yoga classes often emphasize perfecting your alignment or focusing on achieving the external shape of a posture, the goal of therapeutic yoga is not to achieve "perfect" symmetry. Instead, each practice within this book will encourage you to honor your own experience and to listen to your feelings and sensations as wise teachers that will help guide your healing process. Attending to your inner sensations and tuning in to your bodily experience represents the foundation of what is known as embodied self-awareness or embodiment.

Through this process of listening to your body sensations, you will have opportunities to explore how feelings of discomfort can lead you to move in an intuitive manner that helps you to release tension naturally (Fogel, 2009). Rather than overriding your sensations or trying to control your body, the practices in this book invite you to trust your instincts. You can tailor the practices in this book to meet your individual needs through a commitment to listening to your sensations and responding with movements that are unique to you. If at any point your journey toward embodiment feels overwhelming, know that you can seek out the support of a psychotherapist trained in the treatment of trauma, a trauma-informed yoga teacher, or both. In truth, most of us benefit from the caring and compassionate presence of another person who can help us turn toward our pain.

Chapter 1 launches you on your personal journey by introducing a trauma-informed approach to the eight limbs of yoga. The goal of this chapter is to help you focus your attention on the healing power of the present moment. The practices provided will help you orient to safety as you gain comfort with the tools to develop conscious embodiment. In chapter 2, you will learn the neuroanatomy of the mind-body connection that underlies the efficacy of yoga practices. Grounded within the principles of polyvagal theory and affective neuroscience, this chapter will help you gain a greater understanding of how our brains and bodies respond to stress. Moreover, the practices will nourish your nervous system and create greater balance in your body and mind.

Chapter 3 deepens the journey toward embodiment by integrating the principles of somatic psychology and body-oriented therapies into yoga. The practices in this chapter focus on energizing your body with instinctual movements that will help you come out of patterns of freeze, flight, fight, or faint. The progression into chapter 4 invites you to settle your body and mind with restorative practices that evoke a gentle opening of your physical and spiritual heart. Chapter 5 concludes this journey by guiding you to create a personalized yoga practice for your own self-care. If you are a therapist or a yoga teacher, the addendum of this book offers guidance on how to design a sequence of postures for an individual client or student, as well as a framework for creating a six-week therapeutic yoga class for a group of students.

I invite you to open yourself up to this soulful and embodied journey of healing. It is a tremendous honor to be your guide. Each short section of this book concludes with a specific practice to help you apply the theory and integrate the information experientially, with space to reflect and write about your experience. Since your relationship to these practices will likely evolve over time, I invite you to circle back and revisit earlier sections of the book periodically. Your personal writings will serve as markers for your personal transformation. Healing from trauma takes time and requires patience. However, with practice, you can increase your sense of freedom in body and mind. My greatest hope is that you will come away with a lifelong curiosity as you embark on this yogic path of self-discovery.

# The Journey of Practices

• • •

# A Yogic Path for Trauma Recovery

Traumatic events can leave you feeling fragmented, as though you have lost an essential part of yourself. You may feel constantly vigilant or on guard, which is often held as physical tension in the body, as if you are bracing yourself for the next shocking event or terrible loss. You may also have disconnected from your emotions and body sensations as a way to push away difficult feelings and memories from the past. However, pushing away painful feelings also makes it more difficult to feel positive experiences of love, joy, and peace. Healing from trauma invites you to befriend your body, and this needs to occur at a pace that honors your unique needs so you can develop the sufficient resources to eventually turn toward challenging emotions, disturbing symptoms, and distressing memories with compassion.

This chapter introduces you to a yogic path to trauma recovery. Although many people initially think of yoga as a physical practice, it is also a life philosophy that is meant to guide you toward a meaningful and purposeful life. Therefore, this chapter explores a trauma-informed approach to the eight limbs of the yogic path, which include ethical principles, physical postures, conscious breathing, and meditation practices that focus your attention on the healing power of the present moment. With this foundation, you will see that all of the practices offered in this book are reflective of these eight limbs as applied to trauma recovery.

## Trauma Recovery Stages

Trauma recovery occurs in phases. The first phase involves developing a sense of safety in the present moment as you build your capacity to lovingly attend to your emotions and body sensations. The second phase involves turning toward feelings and memories associated with traumatic events. This can bring you to the third phase of trauma recovery, in which you release your burdens as part of a grieving process. This involves letting go of unhelpful beliefs and long-held patterns of tension or energy that have been trapped in your body. Importantly, these three phases of trauma recovery tend to be more circuitous than linear. The goal is not to complete a series of prescriptive steps, but to allow yourself to move freely through these phases, which might involve returning to an earlier phase or experiencing multiple phases simultaneously.

Likewise, a Kripalu yoga practice—which is a gentle form of yoga that encourages you to listen to your body's wisdom as a guide for movement, physical healing, and spiritual transformation—also has three stages that parallel the trauma recovery process. The first stage is referred to as a *willful practice*, as it helps you build both physical stamina and mental focus by moving through postures with an emphasis on strengthening your awareness of your body and breath. At this stage, you reclaim safety as a felt experience of steadiness each time you step on the yoga mat and sense that the earth is supporting you from below. In time, you learn to trust the predictability of the support that your yoga mat provides. This becomes sacred ground and each time you return is a pilgrimage to your body, mind, heart, and soul. During this phase of practice, it can be helpful to give yourself the structure of specific postures or a designated time frame for your practice. Typically, it is recommended that you keep your eyes open during this first stage, as this can help you to stay oriented to cues in the room that remind you that you are safe. It is also fruitful to engage in movement or breathing practices that help you feel empowered and grounded.

The second stage of a Kripalu yoga practice, known as *holding the posture*, invites you to surrender to your inner experience. Now, you shift your attention inside by deepening into shapes for longer periods of time and perhaps closing your eyes to sense the subtle movements of your breath and internal sensations. Deepening involves bringing curiosity to your experience and allowing yourself to be with your sensations and any associations or memories that arise as part of the process. Although you might notice a tendency to assess whether your feelings are "good" or "bad," this stage of practice invites you to explore what happens when you attend to your somatic experience without judgment. Eventually, you might begin to explore an area of tension in your body. For example, you might breathe into a feeling of tension in your chest or throat as you explore an expansive shape that evokes memories of times when guarding your heart may have been necessary. As you release the burdens of traumatic events from your past, it is common for emotions such as grief to arise as part of the healing process. With sufficient support, the tender opening that accompanies the vulnerability of an emotional release can lead to a newly discovered sense of freedom in your body and mind.

Finally, the third stage of the Kripalu practice, *meditation in motion*, is an invitation for you to freely move your body as guided by your sensations. You do so by intuitively following how you want to breathe or move rather than placing yourself within the alignment of any specific yoga posture. This allows you to spontaneously explore the new felt sense of freedom and possibility as you play in the unbounded energy of an open heart. Meditation in motion tends to resolve naturally into stillness. Resting quietly while seated or lying on your back allows you to experience the effects of your practice on your body and mind. Letting go of physical and emotional tension is liberating, but since these defensive holding patterns may have protected you for many years, letting go can also lead you to feel unsettled or unprotected. When this occurs, it can be beneficial to return to the structure of a stage one willful practice. Importantly, as with the phases of trauma recovery, the three stages of a yoga practice are nonhierarchical, and the progression between them may not be linear.

Ultimately, trauma recovery is both a personal and collective journey. Healing from trauma allows you to claim a deep knowing that you belong here in this world, and reclaiming your personal embodiment is deeply interconnected to your relationship with the earth. Yoga invites you to sense and feel your body by attending to the points of contact that your body makes with the ground beneath you and to settle your energy into gravity. In some cases, coming back to the earth leads you to become acutely aware of the historical and ongoing imbalances on the planet, such as climate change and the innumerable atrocities toward indigenous peoples and their lands. Rather than collapsing into hopelessness, yoga can assist you to be of benefit to this hurting world. You develop your capacity to straddle a sense of possibility for a new, improved future while simultaneously allowing yourself to relate to yourself and the world as it is. This tension of opposites becomes fertile soil in which you plant the seeds of change.

With this understanding of the yogic path to trauma recovery, your journey toward healing begins with an invitation to create a safe and sacred space for your practice. I invite you to return to your sacred space each time you work with this book.

## A Sacred Space

In order to heal, you need to feel safe. However, having a history of traumatic events can interfere with your ability to feel safe, calm, or at ease in your mind and body. Healing involves developing a sense of safety in the present moment. Reclaiming this sense of safety can take time, since the body bears the burdens of traumatic events (Scaer, 2014; van der Kolk et al., 2014). A felt sense of safety cannot be forced or faked. You cannot push past your experiences of distress, defensiveness, or tension. Rather, I invite you to recognize that there is intelligence in these reactions and to look for a "safe enough" experience that allows you to attend to your fears, losses, and tender emotions.

To help you create this felt sense of safety, it is helpful to have a calm and peaceful environment for your practice. You might find this within a yoga class, but if you are choosing to begin a home-based practice, I encourage you to take some time to create a space that feels nourishing to your body and mind. This healing space might be a room or area in your home that is quiet, uncluttered, and private enough for you to move and express vulnerable emotions without feeling inhibited. If you live with other people, explore what boundaries you might need to set in order to protect your healing space. For example, is there someone who can watch young children, or could you put a "do not disturb" sign on your door while you are in practice?

This sacred space should also be a place of beauty that is soothing to your senses. You might bring in items from nature, such as flowers, a plant, a beautiful stone, or a seashell. You might also embellish your space with items that have a pleasant scent, such as a candle or an essential oil. You might even use a small table to create an altar upon which to place a few well-chosen items that remind you of the healing purpose of your practice. If you would like to enhance your space through sound, you can play peaceful music or include a small fountain to hear the sounds of moving water. You might also choose to place photographs in your space, such as of yourself as a child as a reminder to send loving-kindness to this part of yourself. Or you might choose a photograph of someone in your life who is or was a nurturing and loving presence.

To support your yoga practice, it is helpful to have a yoga mat, a few blankets for warmth and comfort, one or two yoga blocks, and a yoga strap to help increase accessibility within physical postures. You might also find it beneficial to have a chair in your space as an alternative to sitting on the floor. While these items are recommended, they are not necessary. You can be creative as you develop your own personal yoga practice. For example, instead of a yoga mat you might simply use a towel, you can use books in place of yoga blocks, and you can use a scarf for a yoga strap.

Ideally, your space should feel safe enough for you to relax. Any sacred space, whether it is found in nature or created by humans, provides a sense of solace and respite from the unpredictable or chaotic aspects of life. You can imagine standing by the ocean or walking into a beautiful place of worship. These places invite you to transcend your fears. By creating this baseline of safety, you can observe your body and mind for patterns of tension or changes in breathing that arise as you release trauma-related emotions from your body. If feelings of sadness, fear, or anger arise during your practice, you might choose to direct your attention to sensory details in your space that can help you orient to a sense of ease.

# Create Your Sacred Space

Take a few minutes to write down any ideas you have that will help you to create a healing space. What do you need to do to claim a place in your home for your practice? Are there any items you would like to have in your space, such as flowers, a candle, items from nature, or photographs? What would support you to turn toward difficult emotions? Would you like to listen to music, or do you prefer silence? Once you have identified an ideal environment for your practice, take some time to bring this vision into reality.

---

---

---

---

---

---

---

---

---

---

---

---

---

# The Freedom to Choose

One of the defining features of trauma is loss of choice over what happened to you. Threatening experiences can leave you feeling trapped, helpless, or powerless. Therefore, recovery from trauma involves the realization that you do have choices available to you now. You can choose whether or not to engage in any practice, and you can end the practice at any time. Throughout each practice, you can decide how to move and breathe. This is especially important if you did not have those choices during a traumatic event. You can decide whether you want your eyes open or closed. Since yoga can be relaxing and soothing, or energizing and invigorating, you can vary the practices you choose to meet your needs on any given day.

Exploring these choices on the yoga mat is an essential part of the healing process and can help you remember the many choices available to you when you are out in the world. For example, you can choose what to eat, what to watch on television, or when to go to sleep at night. By paying attention to your body, you can align each of these choices to enhance your physical health, relieve stress, and better support your well-being. Each of these choices allows you to refine how you spend your precious time in ways that feel nourishing to you.

Within his trauma-sensitive yoga program, David Emerson (2015) emphasizes the importance of choice as a prerequisite for safety. When you do not feel as though you have a choice, you can begin to feel trapped, and immediately your nervous system perceives a threat. Focusing on choice facilitates a felt experience of empowerment. This is especially important if you tend to feel stuck in feelings of powerlessness or helplessness. The phrases in the next practice are offered as reminders of the many choices available to support your personal practice. If you are a yoga teacher, these phrases will help you to guide your students, as it is important to be mindful of the language you use when guiding others through a therapeutic yoga practice. Emerson advises using "invitational language" rather than directing a student or client into a pose. For example, you can offer statements such as "See if you would like to lift your arms over your head" or "Notice how you feel as you create this shape with your body." Remember, yoga is about coming home to your true nature.

# Choice and Freedom

Let's look at some examples of statements that encourage choice in a yoga practice:

- No person looks the same in any yoga posture.
- The outer look of the shape isn't our goal.
- You have permission to adapt and change how you move your body at any time.
- You can opt out of this [yoga posture, breath practice, meditation practice, etc.].
- Your eyes can be open or closed.
- See how you want to breathe in this shape.
- See how it feels to make this shape your own.
- Allow yourself to tune in to your inner experience.
- How would you like to move your body now?
- Let your sensations be your guide.
- You can take breaks as needed.
- See how it feels to focus your eyes on one thing that helps you feel calm and peaceful.
- Explore moving your hands into any position that helps you to feel grounded in the present moment.
- Is there any word or short phrase that you would like to say to yourself right now to help focus your mind on a positive intention?

Take a moment to notice how you feel as you reflect on these phrases that encourage you to trust the wisdom of your body as the foundation of your practice. If you would like, write down your reflections and any additional choices that you would like to include to support your practice.

_____

_____

_____

_____

_____

_____

_____

_____

_____

_____

_____

_____

_____

_____

_____

_____

_____

# The Eight Limbs of Yoga

## Limb 1: Seeds of Change (Yamas)

Within the classic yogic text *The Yoga-Sūtra of Patañjali*, which dates back to approximately the fourth or fifth century, we are taught the eight limbs of a yogic path, which include ethical principles, physical postures, breath awareness, and guidance about how to deepen into meditation (Patañjali, 2003). The first of these limbs is the five yamas. The Sanskrit word *yama* means "control," but the five yamas are better understood as ethical and moral principles that help you create a kind, honest, and respectful relationship with yourself and the world.

---

### The Five Yamas

1. *Ahimsa*: nonviolence
2. *Asteya*: non-stealing
3. *Aparigraha*: non-greed
4. *Bramacharya*: moderation
5. *Satya*: truthfulness

---

The first yama is *ahimsa*, which translates to "noninjury" or "nonviolence" in your thoughts and actions. The next two yamas—*asteya* and *aparigraha*—mean "non-stealing" and "non-greed." One way to think about these principles is that they invite you to let go of the belief that you are insufficient, or that you do not have enough, because such beliefs can lead you to take more than you need. You can imagine pouring tea into a cup that is cracked. No matter how much you pour in, you will never fill your cup. Likewise, when you grasp for things, food, or people to make up for an underlying sense of lack, you will never feel fulfilled. Yoga invites you to attend to any underlying wounds that fuel these inaccurate beliefs so you can let go of any tendency to endlessly reach for more.

The fourth yama, *bramacharya*, refers to the process of aligning your actions and behaviors with your highest self or soul. From a trauma-informed perspective, this principle advises you to use your energy wisely so you can best take care of yourself. Most of us have tendencies to give our energy away. For example, this can occur when you are taking care of or focused on pleasing others while sacrificing your own needs. Or maybe you spend too much time scrolling the internet or binge-watching television shows. Bramacharya invites moderation. Now, with awareness, you observe where and how you spend your time so you can redirect your energy to best serve your physical and spiritual well-being. The fifth yama, *satya*, invites you to remain truthful and honest with yourself about your feelings, thoughts, and actions. Being honest helps you recognize your needs, honor your limitations, and set boundaries with those who do not treat you with respect.

The yamas are the beginning of a profound journey, one that invites you to go within and discover the truth of who you are. They assist with trauma recovery because they ask you to develop a deeper relationship to yourself—one that exists beyond the roles you play in your life or the beliefs you carry about yourself. All of us learn behaviors and internalize thoughts about ourselves and the world. Some of these beliefs or behaviors create a greater sense of freedom and possibility, whereas others can lead us to feel more constricted and fearful. Childhood trauma in particular can lead you to internalize negative or hurtful beliefs about yourself and the world. For example, if you were criticized, put down, or shamed growing up, you might carry faulty beliefs that you are unlovable or unworthy of joy. Or you might inaccurately conclude that you'll never belong in this world. You might also feel distrustful of and guarded around other people. Left unaddressed, these early experiences can lead you to perpetuate hurtful behaviors toward yourself or others.

One way that you can integrate the yamas into your yoga practice is by setting an intention, which helps you focus your energy and gives meaning to your practice. In Sanskrit, an intention is called a *sankalpa*. *San* refers to a "connection with your highest truth," while *kalpa* is translated as "vow." You can integrate an intention into any yoga practice by choosing a word, sound, or short phrase (called a *mantra*) that aligns with how you want to live. For example, if your goal is to be less self-critical, your mantra might be "I love and accept myself as I am." Or, if you tend to feel distracted or disconnected from yourself, it might be "I am present." If it is difficult to find words to focus your mind, you can explore how it feels to use the sound of *om* as a way to arrive on your yoga mat. *Om* can be translated to mean the essence of life, and using this sound as an intention can allow you to simply receive the vibration of the feeling of the mantra, allowing the mind to rest.

Ultimately, your intention provides the energy behind your actions in the world so you can become the person you are meant to be. You might work with the same intention in your practice for many months or even years. Or you might feel the need to change your intention as you grow. Most importantly, once you have set your intention, give yourself permission to surrender and trust that you have set an important process in motion. Like planting a seed in the garden of your mind, this intention holds the potential for your visions and dreams. Just as you cannot rush or force the growth of the seed, you must allow the full expression of your intention to occur when the time is right.

Often change is subtle. It doesn't happen all at once. Change accumulates until suddenly your perspective has shifted. Like the subtle ways that the sun's arc in the sky transitions us from winter to spring and then summer, the awakening of your light occurs over time. There may be dark days that require you to have faith in the possibility of generosity and love. However, day by day, your intentions and actions will shape your life. It is through this active engagement with your ideals that you create personal change and help shape a wiser and kinder world.

# Intention Setting

I invite you to create an intention to support your growth. The following questions can help you to choose your word or phrase: What are you ready to change or let go of at this time in your life? What would you like to cultivate more of? What would help you to become the best version of yourself?

Here are some ideas that can help you get started:

- I am present.
- I am listening to my body.
- I am courageous, empowered, and strong.
- I can handle this challenge.
- I am important.
- I deserve to take time for me.
- I love and accept myself as I am.
- I am wise.
- I am resilient.
- I am joyful.
- I am calm and at ease.
- I am supported.
- I am relaxed.
- *Om.*

If you have history of trauma, you might find it difficult to access these positive feelings or beliefs about yourself. However, it is your birthright to be loved. You are and always were worthy of care, kindness, generosity, and attention. I invite you to align yourself with this truth as you take some time to write down your own intentions, either inspired from this list or customized to meet your needs.

_____

_____

_____

_____

_____

_____

_____

_____

_____

_____

_____

_____

_____

If nothing comes to mind when you aim to set an intention, then I invite you to practice with an intention of curiosity. Having an open mind is a powerful intention in itself. Once you have chosen an intention, I invite you to say your word or phrase out loud, or to yourself, two or three times prior to beginning each practice. This will help give meaning to any physical practice of yoga by anchoring you to a feeling of greater depth. At the end of your practice, take a moment to revisit your intention, and notice any small markers of change in your body and mind.

## Limb 2: Know Thyself (Niyamas)

The *niyamas*—which form the second limb of yoga—are five ethical guidelines that refine your relationship to yourself and the world. The first niyama is *saucha*, translated as "cleanliness," which guides the choices you make about how you treat yourself and others. For example, saucha might help you become aware of your overreliance on sugar, media, or substances, which allows you to then create changes that facilitate greater balance and health. Saucha also involves taking personal responsibly for your thoughts and behaviors so you are living in greater alignment with your soul's purpose.

The second niyama is *santosha*, which is contentment. Santosha encourages you to realize that you are whole and that you have enough. Rather than feeling the need to grasp for more, you are invited to appreciate the sweetness of life even though there are inevitable times of pain and loss. During such challenging times, you can draw upon the third niyama, *tapas*, which invokes a disciplined approach to self-transformation. Traumatic events can leave you feeling helpless and as though nothing you do will make a difference in the outcome of your life. *Tapas* refers to the ways that some yoga practices help stoke an inner fire, which becomes the fuel that helps you move out of stagnancy.

The fourth niyama is self-study or *svadhyaya*, which involves observing the thoughts, feelings, and behaviors that arise in response to your inner or outer circumstances. Self-study allows you to cultivate the wisdom that refines any habitual or "knee-jerk" reactions into well-chosen responses. Any disciplined approach to personal transformation needs to be complemented by acceptance of yourself as you are, leading to the fifth niyama, *ishvara pranidhana*, which invites you to surrender and let go of the aspects of life that you cannot change. Often, when you let go of the need to control the outcome of your process, you create space for something new and unexpected to arise. To surrender involves trusting your intrinsic wisdom to guide your healing journey.

### The Five Niyamas

1. *Saucha*: cleanliness
2. *Santosha*: contentment
3. *Tapas*: self-discipline
4. *Svadhyaya*: self-reflection
5. *Ishvara pranidhana*: surrender to a higher power

The accumulated effect of the niyamas is the development of self-knowledge. The Sanskrit word *jnana* and the English word *know* both have etymological roots in the Greek word *gnosis*. Inscribed upon the entrance to the ancient Greek temple of Apollo at Delphi were the words *know thyself*. This phrase can be thought of an invitation to study your own character—both your limitations and your strengths. Rather than ignoring your personal limitations or vulnerabilities, you can cultivate self-knowledge as a way to best attend to your emotional, mental, and physical health.

Becoming a compassionate witness to your body and mind provides a powerful foundation for self-knowledge. At times, your body might react to a stressful event even before you are aware of the trigger. Even without your conscious awareness, your nervous system releases a cascade of stress chemicals, such as cortisol and adrenaline, into your body. This is one reason why you cannot simply think your way out of the symptoms of trauma; rather, you must work with the body to maximize healing, and a regular yoga practice can play an instrumental role in this process.

Through the process of svadhyaya, or self-study, you can practice paying attention to signs that your body is responding to a threat and moving into a defensive state. For example, you might notice that you furrow your brow, tighten your jaw, grip your hands, or clench your buttocks. Sometimes you might have anxiety or react defensively in situations that are actually safe. Conversely, other times, you might miss cues that indicate when situations or people are actually dangerous. Over time and with practice, you can fine-tune your nervous system away from these habitual and conditioned ways of reacting to your world. You can practice building this internal awareness every time you engage in a yoga practice and use this information to better take care of yourself by engaging in practices that either reenergize or relax your mind and body.

Importantly, there is no state of your nervous system that is bad, wrong, or damaged. Rather, the state of your nervous system gives you access to different emotions and sensations. For example, if you are in a defensive state, you might feel your pulse in your chest or notice that your breath has become shallow. Once you increase your perception of these sensations, you can begin to discern whether the response you are having is a reflection of an area in your present-day life that is leading you to feel unsafe. If you are indeed in a situation that feels threatening, you can best determine a course of action that helps you protect yourself. For example, you might explore setting a boundary with someone who is being disrespectful or choose to end a relationship with someone who is harmful to you.

On the other hand, if your defensive reaction is connected to memories of difficult times in the past, you may not yet have the capacity to turn toward these feelings and memories. However, you can build that capacity over time. As needed, you can choose to look around your space and realize that there is no current threat. This can allow you to let go of unnecessary defensive reactions by finding a posture that helps you release emotional tension or by connecting to your breath in a way that helps calm down your nervous system.

As you embark on this courageous journey of embodiment, I invite you to try the following centering practice, which involves observing your body for feedback that suggests you are in a defensive state. Many yoga practices begin and end with a centering practice such as this. Centering can help you feel grounded and oriented to the present moment and aware of your body, mind, emotions, and breath. As part of this practice, I also invite you to notice cues that signal that you feel relaxed and at ease. In time, such awareness will help you let go of unnecessary tension during times of rest.

# Orienting and Centering

This practice invites you to cultivate awareness of your body as you arrive on your yoga mat. When you have a history of trauma, it can be helpful to orient to your space before beginning your practice. This will allow you to turn your attention inward with greater ease so you can observe your body and breath, and ultimately develop a deeper connection to your center. I invite you to set an intention to explore this practice with curiosity and without judgment.

Take a moment to arrive on your mat and look around your space. You can turn your head to the right and left, and you might even turn your whole body to observe the space behind you. Notice any cues that serve as reminders that this is a safe and sacred healing space.

Begin to notice to whether it feels easy or difficult for you to sit still. Are you moving more or less than usual? Do you feel the urge to fidget? Do you feel restless or jittery? Do you feel lethargic or sluggish? Do you feel collapsed or slumped? Do you feel frozen or excessively still? Do you feel relaxed and at ease?

Notice how much space you want to take up right now. Do you feel expansive, or do you feel an urge to curl up and make yourself small?

Begin to notice how you are breathing. Do you notice a tendency to hold your breath? Are you breathing in a shallow manner? Does your breath feel quickened, or do you notice a shortness of breath, like you cannot get enough oxygen? Are you breathing freely and easily?

Do you notice your heartbeat? Does this feel rapid or accelerated? Are you sweating more than usual? Notice the overall quality of your energy. Do you feel vigilant and on high alert? Do you feel foggy or fatigued? Do you feel relaxed and at ease?

Shifting your awareness to your face, do you notice any tension around your eyes? Are they narrowed, or is your brow furrowed? Do you have tension in your forehead or around your temples?

Now bring awareness to your jaw and mouth. Do you notice that you purse your lips or clench your teeth together? Is your tongue pressed firmly against the roof of your mouth? If you'd like, gently move your head around from left to right, then lift and lower your chin. Notice if you feel any tension in your throat, your neck, or the base of your skull. Perhaps roll your shoulders forward and backward, and notice any tightness or constriction around your shoulders, upper back, or chest.

Bring awareness to your belly. Do you notice any tension around your diaphragm, stomach, or lower back? You might explore some gentle movements of your spine—moving forward and backward or side to side—to bring greater awareness to these areas of your body.

If you feel comfortable, bring awareness to your pelvis and hips. Do you notice a tendency to clench the gluteal muscles in your buttocks or to grip in your pelvic floor? Then notice your legs and feet, and see if you tend to carry tension by gripping the muscles in your thighs. Perhaps you carry habitual tension in your calf muscles. Do you tend to grip your feet or curl your toes?

Now, gather a general sense of your body. See if you can welcome yourself just as you are in this moment. Then I invite you to connect to your center by bringing your hands to the center of your chest. Allow the knuckles of your thumbs to press gently into your sternum, awakening sensation in your heart center. This is *anjali mudra*, and it represents a loving honoring of the present moment. Within anjali mudra, the palms are not fully touching—rather, there is a slight space. Gaze down toward your hands, and notice the slight space between your palms resting over your heart. Your hands represent a flower that is not yet open and symbolize your potential to awaken the heart. The act of

gazing down toward your heart symbolizes humility. Take a few breaths to notice any subtle shifts in your body and mind.

When you feel complete, write down any observations that you noticed about yourself during this orienting and centering practice.

_____

_____

_____

_____

_____

_____

_____

_____

_____

_____

_____

_____

_____

_____

_____

_____

_____

_____

## Limb 3: Trauma and the Body (Asana)

The third limb of yoga is *asana*, which is the physical practice of poses. Within yoga for trauma recovery, the goal is not to perfect any external physical posture. Instead, each pose provides an exploratory dive into your own unique experience on the mat. A therapeutic approach to asana invites you to listen to your body and to meet yourself on the mat where you are. Cultivating awareness of your sensations helps you access an internal source of wisdom that guides your healing process. When you have a history of trauma, any embodiment practice can be a vulnerable undertaking. We cannot deny the impact of unresolved trauma on the body. It is often said that "our issues are in our tissues" and that they impact how we move and breathe. Therefore, turning inward takes courage and a leap of faith that recovery is possible.

With asana, you are cultivating the willingness to be open to your experiences and to yourself just as you are (Hayes, 2005). However, willingness can feel counterintuitive. Being human is messy and complex, and we are hardwired to avoid uncomfortable feelings. Difficult emotions such as sadness, anger, fear, hatred, shame, and guilt can feel uncomfortable, confusing, or intolerable. You might notice a desire to avoid or escape these emotions. On the yoga mat, this can arise as fidgeting, being "in your head," feeling distracted, or pushing yourself physically in a way that overrides your sensations. In time, your yoga practice will help you slow down and be present with yourself in the midst of discomfort. This allows you to consciously choose how you would like to respond to distress.

Since vulnerable feelings cannot be entirely eliminated, the practice of yoga also involves learning to accept, rather than merely tolerate, the presence of your own painful emotions. With acceptance, you can recognize that your emotions and sensations are not permanent; rather, they come and go like waves on the ocean. You can learn to surrender and trust these rhythms. Ultimately, the practice of yoga invites you to find a sweet spot between willfulness and acceptance. Within the Kripalu yoga tradition, *will* and *surrender* are described as polarities that need to exist in balance. You can imagine these qualities as the two wings of a bird that need to work in tandem to create flight. In time, you can learn to let go and trust your own capacity to be with yourself in a loving way.

To build your capacity for asana, it is helpful to begin with a stage one willful practice that helps you feel confident in your steadiness and physical strength. There is a strong connection between our physical posture and our sense of empowerment. This idea was popularized by a TED Talk given by Amy Cuddy, whose Harvard-based research found that individuals who embodied an expansive "high-power pose" felt more assertive, more confident, and less reactive to stress than those who assumed a "low-power pose" (Carney et al., 2010; Cuddy et al., 2018). A high-power pose typically involves sitting or standing with your legs slightly wider than your hips and with your hands on your hips, behind your head, or up in the air.

Within yoga, standing postures such as mountain, warrior, and triangle poses can be thought of as power poses. They awaken a connection to your inner strength, which allows you to cultivate mental focus and physical vitality as you engage in a willful practice. You can think of this as the courageous path of the spiritual warrior, in which you develop the discipline to keep showing up for yourself. You assert a commitment to self-love even in the midst of anger, fear, hurt, and shame. You stand up for your worthiness to be loved, cared for, respected, and protected. The following practice invites you to experience these yogic power poses for yourself as you awaken the spiritual warrior within.

# Steadiness and Strength

This practice invites you to explore yogic power poses while standing up, but you can also explore variations of these postures while seated in a chair.

## Orienting and Centering

To begin, find a comfortable position either seated in a chair or standing. I invite you to begin by noticing how you feel right now. This will serve as a baseline and will allow you to notice subtle changes in how you feel throughout the practice.

## Mountain Pose

Now, I invite you to explore the relationship between your feet and the ground beneath you in a mountain pose. Focusing on your connection to the earth provides the foundation for the other yoga postures in this short sequence of poses. It is ideal to explore this practice without shoes on. Allow your arms to simply rest by your sides, and take a moment to wiggle your toes or move your feet in any way that helps you feel connected to the yoga mat or floor beneath you. Now, notice how it feels to rock your weight forward toward your toes, then allow yourself to press into your heels by rocking your weight back. If you are seated, lift your heels to press into the balls of your feet, then lift your toes to press into your heels.

Now, notice how it feels to lift your inner arches, which will press your weight into the outer edges of each foot, and then press into the inside edges of each foot while noticing the sensations in your legs. Take a moment to lift up your toes and spread them wide as you place them back down to the earth to provide a broadened connection to the ground. What do you notice in your legs? How does this change your connection to the earth beneath you? What do you notice emotionally or mentally as you explore these subtle changes between your feet and the ground between you? Now, begin to explore finding the center of your feet so you are not weighted forward toward your toes or back toward your heels and you are not pressing on either the outer or inner edges of your feet. You might rock forward and back and side to side until you discover a felt sense of pressing evenly into your feet. Notice how it feels to sit or stand strong like a mountain.

## Yogic Power Poses

See if you can recall a time when you felt strong, successful, or confident. When you think about this time, what do you notice in your body? Allow yourself to cultivate this feeling in your body. How does your posture naturally change as you reflect on this time? Now, I invite you to explore a traditional power pose while noticing the effects this has on your mental and emotional state. Bring your feet wider than your hips at any distance that helps you feel strong and empowered. Then bring your hands to your hips, and lift your chest slightly. Take a few breaths here and notice how you feel inside. After about a minute, you might choose to bring your arms up over your head in a V shape. Notice how you naturally breathe in this shape. Once again, stay here for a few breaths and then release your hands down. Take a moment to check in with your body.

## Warrior Two

If you are standing, step your feet even wider so you can come into a lunge shape for a warrior two pose. I'll guide you to start on your right side by turning your right toes toward the short side of your yoga mat, in line with your knee, and allowing your left toes to angle forward. Now lunge to the right, bending your right knee over your right ankle, lengthening out through your left leg. Allow yourself to find a depth to this shape that works for you. Know that you can adjust the position of your feet and legs until it feels right to you. If you are seated in a chair, explore shifting your weight onto your right leg as you turn your body to the side, which will allow your left leg to extend back behind you.

In either the standing or seated shape, you can explore how it feels to bring your arms parallel to the ground as you explore this lunge shape. Remember, the feeling of the posture is more important than what you look like from the outside. For this practice, which is focused on steadiness and strength, I invite you to keep your eyes open as you gaze toward your right fingertips. If at any point you notice that you have lost your connection to the earth, bring your attention back to your feet. Continue for about five breath cycles, and then switch to the left side by turning your feet and legs in the opposite direction and lunging to the left.

## Triangle Pose

The triangle shape is considered to be one of the strongest and most stable shapes. It allows you to expand throughout your chest and arms while maintaining a stable base. From the wide-legged stance of your warrior base, turn back toward your right leg, but this time lengthen out through both legs. Once again, your right toes will face toward the short side of your mat while your left toes will angle slightly toward the front of your mat. It is wise to keep a small bend in your right knee to prevent you from hyperextending your joints.

Begin to firmly engage through the muscles of both legs as you inhale, drawing both arms parallel to the ground. On the exhalation, reach your right fingertips out over your right leg and rotate your arms to place your right hand on your right shin, a block, or your yoga mat. As you inhale, allow your left arm to reach up toward the ceiling as you feel the strength of your core while lengthening your torso. Depending on what feels supportive for your neck, you can choose to gaze up toward your left hand, straight ahead, or down toward your right foot. Continue for about five breath cycles, and then switch to the left side by turning your feet and legs in the opposite direction.

## Completion

When you feel complete, come back to standing with your feet beneath your hips. Take several breaths here while noticing your sensations, emotions, thoughts, and level of energy. I recommend that when you complete this active practice, you allow yourself to rest in stillness in a seated position or by lying down on your yoga mat. When you feel complete, take some time to write down any observations, knowing that you can return to this practice as often as you would like.

_____

_____

_____

_____

_____

_____

_____

_____

_____

_____

_____

_____

_____

_____

## Limb 4: Conscious and Intentional Breathing (Pranayama)

The fourth limb of yoga is *pranayama*, which is conscious breathing. Conscious breathing means that you listen and connect to your truth and the wisdom inherent in your body. The Sanskrit word *prana* refers to the breath as connected to your vital life-force energy, whereas *ayama* refers to liberation. In this context, we can think of pranayama as a practice to liberate your vital life-force energy. Traumatic events certainly impact the way we breathe, but in truth, most of us have developed habits of imbalanced breathing as we navigate the unavoidable stressors of life. Perhaps you tend to inhale sharply, which can exacerbate feelings of anxiety. Or maybe you breathe shallowly, which can inhibit your ability to feel your emotions. Or you might have a tendency to hold your breath, which can correspond with difficulty in letting go or fully expressing your feelings.

When you have a history of trauma, simply connecting to your breath might bring up difficult emotions or memories from the past. Connecting to your breath as part of the healing process can be a powerful healing tool, but it may feel difficult to trust this process, especially when your sensations are uncomfortable. While some degree of discomfort is a sign that you are awakening your body-mind connection, it is important to remember that healing requires that you have sufficient support. When exploring any breath practice, it is important to know that you can take breaks and return as you feel ready.

By engaging in conscious breathing, you have the capacity to regulate your autonomic nervous system (we will discuss this in greater depth in chapter 2). For example, deep, slow belly breaths promote feelings of comfort and relaxation while decreasing anxiety, depression, and anger (Zaccaro et al., 2018). In contrast, rapid breaths accompanied by movements of your abdominal muscles can facilitate alertness and enhance stress resiliency (Telles et al., 2011). There are many different breathing patterns taught in pranayama, each of which serves us in a different way. Some are energizing, some facilitate relaxation, some are cleansing, and some create a balanced mind and body. Many involve altering the length of your inhalations and exhalations. You can draw on these different strategies at different times to facilitate your well-being.

As you experiment with all of the breathing techniques offered in this book, you will learn to listen to your body's feedback about which practices serve your goals at any given moment. Some pranayama practices involve holding the breath in at the top of your inhalation or holding the breath out at the end of your exhalation. Keep in mind, these retentions of the breath might be particularly triggering if you experienced events in the past where your breathing was restricted or limited. The practice of therapeutic yoga for trauma recovery invites you to realize that you have a choice about how to breathe and to study how different breath practices change how you feel in your body and mind.

The next foundational practice invites you to explore *dirgha pranayama*, which is the yogic three-part breath. This breath invites you to sequentially expand your belly, rib cage, and upper chest on the inhalation and sequentially release each area of your body on the exhalation. The diaphragmatic expansion of this breath facilitates a relaxation response (Benson & Proctor, 2011; Wang et al., 2010).

# Three-Part Breath

I encourage you to study the effect that this three-part yogic breath practice has on your body and mind.

### Orienting and Centering

To begin, find a comfortable seat in a chair or on the floor. I invite you to begin by noticing how you feel right now. This will serve as a baseline and will allow you to notice subtle changes in how you feel throughout the practice.

### Three-Part Breath

Bring one or both hands over your navel and focus on each inhalation into your lower lungs, expanding your belly like a balloon with each inhalation, and then exhaling as you release your breath and belly. Continue to take several breaths in this manner. When you feel ready to add the second part of this breath practice, take your hands to your rib cage. This time, as you inhale, fill your belly and then fill your ribcage, which will expand your diaphragm. As you exhale, release the breath from your ribcage and then from your belly. Continue to breathe in this manner for several breaths. If you would like, you can explore adding the third part of this breath practice by placing your hands over your chest.

Now, as you inhale, begin by filling your belly, ribcage, and chest, and then exhale as you release your chest, ribcage, and belly. Continue to breathe in this manner for about two more minutes.

## Completion

Slowly release the breath practice. What are you aware of now as you notice your body, mind, emotions, and level of energy? Take some time to write down any observations, knowing that you can return to this practice as often as you would like.

_____

_____

_____

_____

_____

_____

_____

_____

_____

_____

_____

_____

_____

_____

## Limbs 5 and 6: Dual Awareness and Trauma Recovery
## (Pratyahara and Dharana)

The fifth limb of yoga is *pratyahara*, which refers to the practice of turning the focus of your attention inward by gently softening or closing your eyes. This inward shift redirects your attention so you can notice your internal sensations. From a yogic perspective, you can think of this process as directing your life-force energy toward yourself. Ideally, this provides a respite from the outer world and is a way to nourish yourself with self-awareness.

The sixth limb of yoga is *dharana*, which is the practice of immersing yourself in the present moment through focused concentration. Like pratyahara, it also directs your attention away from the stimulation of the outer world. However, dharana involves focusing your eyes on a single point, called a *drishti* in Sanskrit. When we feel restless, it is common for our eyes to jump from one object to another, which can make it difficult for the mind to rest. In contrast, when we allow our eyes to rest on a single point, such as a place on the floor in front of you, the mind and body can begin to settle into stillness. Dharana can also be practiced by focusing your mind on your hands in a specific position, such as in anjali mudra, or by looking at your fingertips.

Drawing your senses away from the outer world can be challenging when you have a history of trauma. Hypervigilance heightens your senses and can lead you to become highly attuned to your surroundings. You might feel jumpy, be sensitive to loud noises, or be highly reactive to crowded spaces. You might scan the people around you by reading their facial expressions, voice tone, or body language. Or you might scan your environment for potential signs of threat or an exit strategy. When you have had to attend to your environment for extended periods of time, your attentional focus can start to feel stuck in this manner. You might find it difficult to let down your guard because you fear that you will be unable to protect yourself without it. Or you might fear that your body will begin to relax, which gives you greater access to your emotions. In short, letting go of your defenses can feel vulnerable.

One way to build your capacity to turn your attention inward is by cultivating dual awareness. Dual awareness involves noticing environmental cues that let you know you are safe now while simultaneously paying attention to uncomfortable sensations or emotions for brief periods of time (Rothschild, 2010). For example, you might look around your healing space and focus your eyes on external cues of safety, such as the sky outside your window, until you feel calm and at ease. Then you might begin to orient your attention to your body. It can help to start by noticing the feeling in your fingers and toes, the movement of air through your nose as you breathe, or the shape of your body as you practice yoga.

As you continue, you might feel more capable of paying attention to your internal sensations, such as the temperature of your body or the feeling of your breath moving in and out of your belly. If at any point an emotion or sensation feels overly distressing, you can return your attention to your external cues of safety. Eventually, you might feel comfortable paying attention to patterns of physical tension or the weight of any emotional burdens you carry. Most importantly, be gentle with yourself.

The next practice invites you to explore dual awareness within child's pose. For some, the name *child's pose* brings up discomfort because it evokes memories from a vulnerable time. If this is the case, you can choose to rename this pose, giving it a new meaning for you. For example, you might call it *wisdom* or *resting pose*.

# Resting in Child's Pose

This posture invites you to turn your attention inward within the resting shape of child's pose with guidance to practice dual awareness. Traditionally, child's pose is an invitation to rest on the floor with your hips toward your heels. If you prefer, explore a variation of this shape while seated in a chair with a bolster or pillow.

## Orienting and Centering

To begin, find a comfortable seat in a chair or on the floor, and notice your body sensations, your breath, and any emotions that are present for you in this moment. Remember, you can take your time with this part of the practice by looking around the room. Begin to notice your sensations, emotions, thoughts, and level of energy. This will serve as a baseline and will allow you to notice subtle changes in how you feel throughout the practice.

## Child's Pose

If you would like to explore child's pose on your yoga mat, bring yourself into a tabletop shape with your hands below your shoulders and your knees below your hips. If it feels okay to you, begin to settle your hips toward your heels. There is no single right way to create this shape. Take your time to adjust your shape until it feels supportive for you. You might place your knees close together, which will allow your chest to rest on your thighs, or you might choose to widen your knees, which will allow your chest to soften closer to the floor. You might prefer to have a folded blanket or bolster between your hips and your heels to reduce pressure behind your knees. See how it feels to rest your forehead on the floor in front of you or on a soft pillow.

You can also explore whether you prefer to have your arms outstretched in front of you alongside your head or resting back beside your torso. If you prefer a variation of child's pose in a chair, rest the weight of your head onto a bolster or pillow. You can adjust the height of the support until the pose feels nourishing to you. As you find your way into your chosen shape, notice how your belly and vital organs are protected in this shape. See if you can allow the muscles in your neck to relax. How does your mind respond as you slow down? This inward turn invites you to soften your vigilance and let go into a sense of support and safety.

## Dual Awareness

If at any point in this shape you notice that you feel uncomfortable or unsafe, I invite you to remember that you have choices available to you. You can come out of this shape at any time, which will allow you to redirect your attention to a visual cue that helps you feel supported and safe. Perhaps you wiggle your fingers and toes. Are there any other movements that would feel supportive for you here? Perhaps you slowly move your hips from side to side or roll your head, massaging your forehead on the yoga mat or bolster. Notice whether you prefer to keep your eyes open or if you would like to close your eyes in this shape. You could also play soft music as a way to help you stay oriented to the safety of your space as you bring your attention inward.

## Completion

Take a few more deep breaths while in this shape, and whenever you feel ready to come out of it, place your hands underneath your shoulders and slowly press into your hands to lift your spine until you have returned to a seated position. What are you aware of now as you notice your body, mind, emotions, and level of energy? Take some time to write down any observations, knowing that you can return to this practice as often as you would like.

_____

_____

_____

_____

_____

_____

_____

_____

_____

_____

_____

_____

## Limbs 7 and 8: The Wisdom of Pure Awareness
## (Dhyana and Samadhi)

The seventh limb of yoga is *dhyana*, which is the Sanskrit word for meditation. Rather than being an effortful practice, dhyana is better understood as the spontaneous opening of the heart that is the result of the disciplined practices of the previous six limbs. At this stage of practice, you have an opportunity to let go of all effort and simply receive the benefit of your own presence in stillness with a quiet yet awake mind. This process invites a reflective and receptive state of awareness.

Opening up to the spacious quality of dhyana can feel challenging when you have a history of trauma. Reflexively, your mind might grow active, or your body might feel restless. Rather than fighting these impulses, you learn to witness or observe these fluctuations of your mind. In time, you will discover a quiet space that exists below the chatter of your mind, beyond the roles that you play in the world, and beneath the wounds that you have experienced. Yoga ultimately invites you into this deep, inner knowing of your true self. This is the eighth limb of yoga, *samadhi*, which is a unified state of pure awareness that allows you to be fully immersed in the present moment.

While samadhi might sound unachievable, in reality most of us have experienced this state of being at some point or another. Perhaps you have felt this quality of meaningful sense of connection with yourself at a time when you fully accepted yourself without judgment and, as a result, felt an outpouring of compassion for others. Or maybe you felt a sense of deep peace while walking in nature when you suddenly noticed the vibrancy and beauty of the colors and sounds around you. Maybe you have felt a spontaneous upwelling of gratitude during a meditation practice. Or perhaps you can reflect on moments in your life that have evoked emotions of awe, joy, peace, bliss, and hope. In these moments, we temporarily let go of an illusion of separateness.

From a yogic perspective, the root cause of suffering is not knowing the truth of who you are. However, with samadhi, you can discover and align yourself with an unwavering sense of self—a sort of inner witness—who is capable of nonjudgmentally witnessing your thoughts, emotions, or sensations. By connecting to this wise self, you can turn toward your experience with curiosity and respond compassionately and courageously to distressing emotions or memories (Schwartz, 1997). For example, you might begin to observe self-critical thoughts, or you might notice a habitual way of breathing and moving that worsens your emotional reactions. Such observations can then allow you to consciously adopt new, more loving ways of talking to yourself or to explore a more satisfying way of breathing and moving your body.

The clarity of this inner witness can help you observe your life with a bird's-eye view that allows you to create distance from your suffering. Stepping back can help you place difficult life events within a larger context of your own life. Not only have you experienced painful losses, but you can also reflect on loving moments of connection and times when you were touched by the beauty of this world. Indeed, being a trauma survivor doesn't mean that you are not eligible for bliss, joy, and peace. Even a brief taste of this spacious grace is a reminder that you carry this potential within you.

While the witness can help you temporarily distance yourself from your distress, the ultimate goal is not to remain detached or disconnected from your emotions and sensations. This is especially important because it is common to feel cut off, disconnected, or dissociated from yourself when you have a history of trauma. Connecting to your inner observing self can ultimately allow you to lovingly attend to your emotions and sensations. Now you can imagine that the wisest version of yourself is holding space for your wounds. Over time, this state of ease becomes easier to access even during the challenging moments of life. In time and with practice, you can learn to live more fully in the present moment, which allows you access to the clarity of your true self and to the wisdom of pure awareness.

The following practice invites you to explore a brief meditation focused on awakening the witness. Here, you will be introduced to another classical *mudra* or hand position called *jnana mudra*, which is associated with knowledge or wisdom.

# Awaken the Witness

I invite you to explore this short practice that is focused on cultivating your inner witness—a wise self who is capable of nonjudgmentally observing your thoughts, emotions, and sensations.

## Orienting and Centering

Find a comfortable place to sit, making sure this is a place where you feel safe. Choose how long you would like to engage in this practice, and if you would like, set a timer to chime as a way to end your practice. I suggest beginning with just three to five minutes, knowing that you can extend the time you spend in meditation as you feel ready. You can choose to practice with your eyes open or closed. When you feel ready, begin to notice your sensations, emotions, thoughts, and level of energy. This will serve as a baseline and will allow you to notice subtle changes in how you feel throughout the practice.

## Jnana Mudra

If you would like, you can come into jnana mudra as a symbolic gesture to connect to your wisest self. To do so, gently touch or slightly tuck the tip of your index finger under to the tip of your thumb while keeping the rest of your fingers extended. You can then explore how it feels to rest your hands on the tops of your thighs with your palms facing up or down. Turning your palms up might feel uplifting, as if you are open to receiving. On the other hand, turning your palms down might feel grounding or comforting. Notice if one or the other feels better for you today. Once you arrive in your version of this mudra, simply notice how the subtlety of this shape impacts the quality of your thoughts, emotions, or energy.

## Cultivating the Witness

Now imagine that you are sitting alongside a river. Whenever a thought, emotion, or sensation arises, see if you can imagine placing it on a leaf and allowing it to flow downstream. Notice if you have a desire to hang on to any particular thought, emotion, sensation, or other story in your mind. Once again, honor this experience without judgment, and perhaps experiment with placing it into the river. There is no need to resist your thoughts, emotions, or sensations. They will continue to come, and this is completely normal. Notice what it is like to allow your experiences to come and go. Notice how it feels to be the witness of your internal experiences.

## Completion

When you are complete with this meditation practice, take a moment to notice what you are aware of now in your body, mind, emotions, and level of energy. Take some time to write down any observations, knowing that you can return to this practice as often as you would like.

_____

_____

_____

_____

_____

_____

_____

_____

## Chapter Review

This chapter provided you with a trauma-informed perspective on the eight limbs of the yogic path. If you would like, take some time to review your written responses to the practices in this chapter. What have learned so far about yourself on this journey of yoga?

_____

_____

_____

_____

_____

_____

_____

_____

_____

_____

_____

_____

_____

_____

_____

_____

_____

The chapter provided you with a basic understanding of the way in which it is to be worth it. Now we will get the same time to do so much work, so now you'll make it to the fullest. We have learned to go through the process in terms of types.

CHAPTER 2

# Applied Polyvagal Theory in Yoga: Practices for Balance and Equanimity

The autonomic nervous system is your body's innate stress response system that regulates basic survival functions such as breathing, heart rate, body temperature, sleep, and digestion. This complex system is made up of two primary branches, the sympathetic and parasympathetic nervous systems, which work in tandem with each other. In response to stress, the sympathetic nervous system increases your heart rate, quickens your breathing, engages muscular tension, and slows down your digestion—all for the purpose of self-protection. You can think of this as a metaphorical gas pedal that mobilizes your body for the purpose of self-protection through the fight-or-flight response. In contrast, when you are safe, the parasympathetic nervous system slows you back down and eases you into a relaxation response, which allows you to rest, digest, and recover from stress.

Ideally, you transition easily and fluidly between these two nervous system states, which allows you to face challenges as needed and recover from stress easily. However, trauma can leave you in a state of chronic stress, causing the sympathetic nervous system to remain active for extended periods of time. This can leave you feeling keyed up with anxiety and interfere with your ability to sleep well at night. The sympathetic nervous system is only meant to function for short periods of time, so when trauma remains unresolved, the body's stress response system begins to break down, leading the parasympathetic nervous system to become dominant. In this case, rather than feeling simply relaxed, you are more likely to feel fatigued, depressed, or shut down.

Stephen Porges has provided us with an even greater understanding of the autonomic nervous system as it relates to trauma and why the parasympathetic system has this paradoxical response to trauma. His polyvagal theory explains how the vagus nerve, which governs the parasympathetic nervous system response, can be divided into two different circuits (Porges, 2011). The most recently evolved circuit of the vagus nerve, called the *ventral vagal complex*, has nerve endings that connect to the muscles around your eyes, mouth, inner ear, larynx, pharynx, heart, and lungs. Porges calls the ventral vagal complex the *social engagement system* because it connects to the parts of your body that are primarily involved in helping you feel socially connected and safe in the world. For example, you express your emotions through your eyes, facial expressions, and voice tone.

There is also an evolutionarily older circuit of the vagus nerve called the *dorsal vagal complex*, which descends through the diaphragm into your digestive organs, including the stomach, spleen, liver, kidneys, and small and large intestines. When you feel safe, this extension of the vagus nerve allows you to rest into stillness, which facilitates your ability to relax, rest, and digest. However, the dorsal vagal complex also functions to immobilize the body in situations involving extreme life threat. This hardwired response moves the body into a state of immobility, dissociation, or numbness when the danger involves on ongoing threat from which there is no escape.

Both the ventral and dorsal vagal branches of the vagus nerve function as a "vagal brake" that subdues or stops the defensive mobilization of the sympathetic nervous system. This process is similar to that of putting the brakes on a car: You can either slow down gradually and smoothly or come to a hard, sudden stop. The ventral vagal complex functions as a fine-tuned brake that allows you to slow down in a smooth manner, which facilitates your rest-and-digest response. However, the dorsal vagal complex serves as an abrupt brake by immobilizing the body into a form of feigned death. When this occurs, you might feel weak, fatigued, dizzy, or nauseous. That's because digestion is costly from a metabiological standpoint, so emptying the digestive tract, slowing down the heart rate, and reducing respiration allows the body to survive a threatening situation for a longer period of time.

According to Porges (2011), the nervous system is constantly assessing whether situations or people are safe, dangerous, or life-threatening, a process that he termed *neuroception*. Even without conscious awareness, your nervous system is always looking for signs of threat—whether it's within your body, in your external environment, or in the body language, facial expressions, and voice tones of other people. In response to those cues, your body automatically adjusts your heart rate, breathing pattern, and level of muscle tone, even though you might not be aware of these changes as they occur. For example, you might react defensively to the sound of someone's voice without fully understanding why you feel agitated.

The vagus nerve plays a key role in neuroception because it sends signals between your body and your brain. The vagus nerve is the tenth cranial nerve and can best be described as a bidirectional communication highway between your body and your brain.

The term *vagus* is Latin for "wandering," which is an apt descriptor for a nerve that extends from the brainstem into the stomach, intestines, heart, lungs, throat, and facial muscles. Approximately 85 percent of vagus nerve fibers are afferent, meaning that they bring sensory information from your body to your brain (Shaffer et al., 2014).

Given the role of the vagus nerve in the autonomic nervous system, learning how to regulate the vagus nerve can improve both your mental and physical health. Not only can it help you more effectively respond to the emotional and physiological symptoms of depression, anxiety, and PTSD, but it may also serve as a potential "off switch" for inflammation-related diseases such as epilepsy, rheumatoid arthritis, and inflammatory bowel syndrome. In the medical field, vagus nerve stimulation, also referred to as *neuromodulation*, involves using an electrical device to send a stimulating, yet undetectable, electrical current to the vagus nerve (Deuchars et al., 2018). However, you can also naturally stimulate the vagus nerve by altering the rhythm of your breath, practicing mindful body awareness, and exploring gentle yoga postures. Remember, your vagus nerve passes through your belly, diaphragm, lungs, throat, inner ear, and facial muscles. Therefore, practices that stimulate or relax these areas of the body can influence the tone of your vagus nerve through the mind-body feedback loop.

To help you create greater health and balance within your autonomic nervous system, this chapter applies polyvagal theory to the practice of yoga through a variety of breath and movement exercises. These practices can help you to find greater ease in your body, clarity of mind, balance for your emotions, satisfaction in your relationships, and spiritual fulfillment.

## Equanimity Amid Change

When you engage in physical postures (asana) and conscious breathing (pranayama) you are practicing *hatha* yoga. *Hatha* is the practice of balancing out the polarities of the solar and lunar elements. Just as the sun is fiery and hot, our solar nature is described as active, creative, willful, and full of vitality. In contrast, the lunar elements are our restful, quiet, introspective, and receptive capacities. In general, yoga practices are designed to balance these polarities in order to cultivate a clear and focused mind in preparation for meditation.

Within the yogic tradition, these aspects of the self are also referred to as the *gunas*, which is a Sanskrit term referring to the states of being that can be found in all things. The first guna is *rajas*, which—like the solar element—is described as movement, momentum, or a spark that starts a fire. While we all have rajasic qualities, an imbalance can lead to restlessness, excessive worry, anxiety, and anger. The second guna is *tamas*, which—like the lunar element—is described as inertia or inactivity. When out of balance, tamas can become a source of stagnancy that can lead you to feel dull, lethargic, fatigued, or depressed. Finally, the third guna is *sattva*, which is described as lightness, clarity, joy, buoyancy, balance, tranquility, peace, and ease. One of the goals of yoga is to cultivate a more sattvic presence. Once again, you are cultivating the connection to your wise, true self.

We can find remarkable parallels between yogic descriptors of the gunas and our scientific understanding of our autonomic nervous system (Sullivan et al., 2018). Like rajas, the sympathetic nervous system mobilizes us to take action in the world, and in times of stress, it helps us protect ourselves through the fight-or-flight response. Like tamas, the ventral vagal branch of the parasympathetic nervous system engages a relaxation response that temporarily suspends the defensive actions of the sympathetic nervous system, which allows the body to rest, digest, and connect intimately with others. However, as highlighted in polyvagal theory, the parasympathetic nervous system also has a dorsal vagal branch that can elicit an immobilization response, which can lead to a feigned death or faint response during times of threat. When this immobilization response continues over an extended period of time, you are more likely to experience the imbalanced expression of tamas as predominant feelings of stagnancy, powerlessness, fatigue, or depression.

You can think of sattva as an optimal expression of your social engagement system that helps you feel calm, curious, connected, and capable of choosing how to respond to a range of feelings and experiences. To achieve this optimal expression, you can blend the social engagement system with either the sympathetic nervous system or the dorsal vagal complex, which engages you in a state of energizing wakefulness or calming restfulness. For example, blending your social engagement system with the sympathetic nervous system helps you connect to excitement, play, and laughter (energizing wakefulness). Whereas rajas alone can lead to agitation and turbulent emotions, when combined with sattva, you are more likely to feel inspired and joyful. On the yoga mat, this blend can help you mobilize your body into active postures, such as downward dog, standing postures, and heart openers. Off the yoga mat, you might find the motivation to engage in meaningful actions toward your personal goals or collective betterment.

You can also blend your social engagement system with the dorsal vagal complex, which allows you to find nourishment in states of stillness and deep relaxation (calming restfulness). Tamas alone can lead to sluggishness or indifference, but when nourished by sattva, you can discover greater stability, groundedness, and spacious awareness during times of stillness. On the yoga mat, this blend can help you soften into restorative poses, such as child's pose, yoga nidra, or the deep spiritual states found in meditation. This can translate into better sleep, improved digestion, and better overall health (Trakroo & Bhavanani, 2016).

An apt metaphor to understand these three states of the autonomic nervous system is found in the childhood fairytale "Goldilocks and the Three Bears." In this story, Goldilocks enters the house of the three bears and tries each of their bowls of porridge, finding that one bowl is too hot, another is too cold, but the third is "just right!" These bowls of porridge correspond with the states of your nervous system. Being "too hot" represents an overactive sympathetic nervous system that might lead you to feel keyed up, anxious, irritable, or panicky. Being "too cold" represents a state of dorsal vagal activation that can lead you to feel shut down, depressed, collapsed, or hopeless. However, by engaging your ventral vagal complex you can find that sweet spot where everything feels "just right."

Keep in mind, though, that there are times when you cannot move directly from a dorsal vagal state into a state of social engagement. When this occurs, you can climb the metaphorical polyvagal ladder out of collapse through mindful mobilization (Dana, 2018). To do so, imagine that the dorsal vagal complex sits at the bottom of the ladder, the sympathetic nervous system in the middle, and the ventral vagal complex at the top. In this case, you would consciously engage the sympathetic nervous system to revitalize your body as a way to move up the ladder. You might accomplish this by standing up, taking several deep breaths, or stretching your body as a way to wake up your nervous system. This would allow you to gradually move toward a state of social engagement found in sattva.

Ultimately, sattva generates a feeling of equanimity. Equanimity involves increasing your ability to stay present and be patient with uncomfortable experiences. Although the only constant in life is change, we so often brace against it. We fear that we will be out of control, groundless, and vulnerable. One way to establish equanimity in the midst of the flux of life is to return to the constancy of the breath, which can allow you to remain connected to your center even when there are elements of your life that are out of your control. An example of a relatively simple breathing exercise that can balance your autonomic nervous system is *sama vritti pranayama*, which involves creating an even length of your inhalations and exhalations. The Sanskrit word *sama* means "same" or "equal," while *vritti* is often translated as "movement," which refers not only to the changes of the breath but also to the fluctuations of the mind.

In addition to balancing the lengths of the inhalation and exhalation, you can facilitate a relaxation response by changing how you breathe. When you feel stressed, you are more likely to breathe with a heavy sigh through your mouth. In contrast, you can evoke inner calm when you breathe through your nose in a slow and soft manner. The balanced breath is light and quiet. You can imagine softening the edges of the breath so there is a gentle transition between each in-breath and out-breath. The following gentle breathing practice will help you to generate an inner feeling of contentment and balance.

# Balanced Breath

This practice involves creating an even length of your inhalations and exhalations. I encourage you to study the effect that this simple practice has on your body and mind.

## Orienting and Centering

To begin, find a comfortable seat in a chair or on the floor. Notice your body sensations, your breath, and any emotions that are present for you in this moment. This will serve as a baseline and will allow you to notice subtle changes in how you feel throughout the practice.

## Balanced Breath

When you are ready, begin by noticing your breath. See if you can sense the weight of your breath. Can you soften the intensity of your breath so it feels lighter and softer? Like a lake on a calm day, your breath would not create any ripples on the surface of the water. Begin to notice the length of your breath, and explore a count of four on each inhalation and a count of four on each exhalation. As you even out the length of your breath, see if you can cultivate a smooth and light sensation by creating soft transitions between each in-breath and out-breath. Perhaps imagine that your breath is flowing along the inside of the perimeter of a circle.

As you grow comfortable with this breath, you can experiment with increasing to a six-count inhalation and exhalation. You might even notice how it becomes easy to pause at the top of your inhalation, as if a feather is floating on the air before gently cascading down. Likewise, see if there is a natural inclination to pause and rest on the empty shallow bed of your exhalation. If you do rest in these pauses, there should be no forcing or holding of your breath. You are savoring the fullness until you feel a natural inclination to exhale. Likewise, allow yourself to rest in emptiness until you feel the natural longing to catch the wave of your next inhalation. Allow this breath pattern to feel effortless. Continue for several minutes or for as long as it feels nourishing for your mind and body.

## Completion

What are you aware of now as you notice your body, mind, emotions, and level of energy? Take some time to write down any observations, knowing that you can return to this practice as often as you would like.

_____

_____

_____

_____

_____

_____

_____

_____

_____

_____

_____

_____

_____

_____

# Conscious Breathing and Vagal Tone

The practice of yoga awakens the spiritual heart. Your physical heart also plays a key role in this process because it harbors an intrinsic nervous system that can produce and secrete hormones and neurotransmitters that had previously only been thought to exist in the brain (Armour, 2008; Shaffer et al., 2014). Within your upper chest, you have a massive convergence of major arteries, veins, and nerves that is called the *cardiac plexus*. These nerve fibers include the vagus nerve, coronary nerves that innervate the heart, pulmonary nerves that extend into the lungs, and laryngeal nerves that connect into the throat. Recall that approximately 85 percent of the vagus nerve fibers are afferent, which means they communicate information from the body to the brain. Moreover, the majority of these nerve fibers travel to the brainstem from the heart and cardiovascular system.

The heart and lungs are deeply interconnected with each other and with the autonomic nervous system, so the breath plays a key role in your health. For example, during times of stress, your sympathetic nervous system will initiate quick, intense breaths into your upper lungs to help you move away from or protect yourself against a threat. When you feel safe once again, your parasympathetic nervous system will then slow down your breathing and heart rate. While these changes in breathing happen automatically in response to stress, you also have the ability to alter your physiology through conscious, mindful changes in the pace and length of your breath. Long, slow exhalations stimulate the vagus nerve, which initiates a parasympathetic relaxation response that calms your body down.

Yogic practices are another way to stimulate your vagus nerve and enhance both vagal efficiency and vagal tone. *Vagal efficiency* refers to how quickly the vagus nerve can help you adapt to everyday stressors. One way to assess vagal efficiency is to look at the impact of simple postural changes—such as shifting from lying down, to sitting, to standing—because this provides a measure of how your heart rate tolerates these movements in relationship to gravity. When you sit or stand, your heart rate must change very quickly to increase your blood pressure so you do not pass out. Therefore, yoga practices that involve controlled changes in your posture as related to gravity can help improve vagal efficiency.

*Vagal tone* refers to the strength of your vagus nerve, and it is measured by changes in heart rate in relationship to the breath. Your heart rate increases on each inhalation, which reflects a subtle engagement of the sympathetic nervous system, and decreases during each exhalation as the parasympathetic nervous system reengages. The relationship between your breath and these changes in heart rate is referred to as *heart rate variability* or *respiratory sinus arrhythmia*. Your heart rate is a measure of the number of beats per minute, whereas heart rate variability is a measure of the intervals between your heartbeats. Low heart rate variability is associated with low vagal tone and a reduced capacity to handle stress. On the other hand, high vagal tone is associated with greater heart rate variability, meaning that you recover from upsetting events with greater ease. You can think of this as the physiological basis for resilience—the ability to flexibly respond to the inevitable challenges of life. Therefore, having a higher vagal tone can lead to improved immune system functioning and greater mental well-being (Brown & Gerbarg, 2005a, 2005b; Rhodes et al., 2016; Seppälä et al., 2014; Tyagi & Cohen, 2016).

However, individuals with a history of trauma often experience disruptions in their autonomic nervous system, known as *dysautonomia*, which can interfere with vagal tone. Dysautonomia typically refers to a rapid drop in heart rate, blood pressure, and muscle tone upon standing. For many, these experiences are followed by sympathetic activation, which can lead to emotional dysregulation or feelings of panic. For some, the dysregulation of the nervous system might lead to a paradoxical response in which they remain immobile and unable to engage in self-protective actions during threatening experiences (Beauchaine, 2001; Suveg et al., 2019).

One of the most efficient ways to improve vagal tone and create a calm body and mind is by changing how you breathe. Conscious breathing can help you cultivate nervous system flexibility so you can tolerate a range of different arousal states while responding effectively and efficiently. The following breath practice emphasizes a long, slow exhalation to produce a parasympathetic response in your body. In this breath, you will exhale through pursed lips shaped like a straw or an O. This action will help you lengthen the out-breath as compared to the in-breath. Engaging the muscles around the mouth also initiates a subtle stimulation of your vagus nerve.

# Straw Breath

I encourage you to study the effect of this breath practice by noticing how you feel emotionally or by observing changes in your state of mind. The straw breath aims to help you engage your parasympathetic nervous system by lengthening your exhalation as compared to your inhalation.

## Orienting and Centering

To begin, find a comfortable seat in a chair or on the floor. Notice your body sensations, your breath, and any emotions that are present for you in this moment. This will serve as a baseline and will allow you to notice subtle changes in how you feel throughout the practice.

## Straw Breath

When you are ready, begin to create a straw shape with your lips. You can practice this breath with a physical straw, as well. To begin, inhale gently. Then purse your lips and exhale very slowly through your imagined straw for a count of eight. Then close your mouth and slowly exhale through your nose for a count of two as you engage the muscles in your abdomen and diaphragm to expel all of the air from your lungs. Allow your next inhalation to come naturally, and take three regular breaths. To counterbalance any overstimulation of the sympathetic nervous system, you can focus on diaphragmatic breathing as you inhale. If you would like, repeat this exercise two or three more times.

## Completion

What are you aware of now as you notice your body, mind, emotions, and level of energy? Take some time to write down any observations, knowing that you can return to this practice as often as you would like.

_____

_____

_____

_____

_____

_____

_____

_____

_____

_____

_____

_____

_____

_____

# Listening and Your Vagus Nerve

The concept of the "third ear" was introduced by psychoanalyst Theodor Reik, who emphasized the importance attending to tone of voice, inflection, and pauses between words and phrases as a way to gather a feeling for what the other person is saying. By listening for these deeper emotional meanings that underlie the words themselves, we increase our ability to hear what is not being said (Reik, 1983). However, listening with the third ear is dependent on your ability to listen to yourself—to your own emotions and sensations. It is only by knowing yourself that you have the tools necessary to understand others.

When we look at the science of how we process sound, we realize that the act of listening is quite a profound process. Sound consists of waves that vibrate the air, enter your auditory canal, and pass through your tympanic membrane, also known as your eardrum. These waves proceed to move three bones within your ear: the malleus, the incus, and the stapes, which is the smallest bone in your body. The sound vibrations then move the fluid of your inner ear, which bends tiny hairs and charges molecules to create electric patterns. The vestibulocochlear nerve, which is the eighth cranial nerve, then helps transmit these electric signals to your brain.

In addition, the vagus nerve plays a key role in this process. When you feel safe and relaxed, there is greater tension in the stapedius and tensor tympani muscles of your inner ear. Having tension in these muscles increases sensitivity to the human voice by reducing sensitivity to high and low frequency background sounds (Porges, 2017). In contrast, when you are experiencing a threat, the tone of the inner ear muscles goes slack, which allows greater sensitivity to those high and low frequency sounds. For example, when you hear a threatening low frequency sound—such as the low growl of an animal or the gruff voice of someone who is angry with you—you experience an immediate full-body sympathetic nervous system response that engages your self-protective defenses. Likewise, high frequency sounds in nature—such as the screeching of monkeys or birds—allow animals to communicate to one another about a potential threat in their environment. Thus, the brain is hardwired to interpret these high and low frequency sounds as dangerous.

At the same time, though, your nervous system is hardwired to respond to the soothing sound of the human voice, such as the sound of a mother singing a lullaby to soothe her infant (Porges & Lewis, 2010). In fact, music is powerful way to stimulate the vagus nerve. These sounds of safety awaken the social nervous system and facilitate full-body experiences of ease. Your vagus nerve communicates this felt sense of safety by relaxing the muscles around the larynx and pharynx in your throat, which allows your voice tone to develop greater prosody through a gentle rising and falling in your speech. When you speak in this manner, you come across as less threatening to others, which reinforces a shared, relational experience of safety. You can think of this as a bidirectional feedback system between your inner ear and your voice that allows you to reduce defensive engagement for the purpose of social connection.

In the yogic tradition, attending to sound has been a central part of many practices. *Nada yoga* is the yoga of sound, which is a practice of listening receptively to the sounds around you. For example, you might explore a listening meditation while sitting by the seashore, deeply immersing yourself in the sounds of the waves. Yoga also incorporates sound meditations, such as chanting or listening to the sound of singing bowls and gongs to create a sound bath. In addition, *bhramari pranayama*, which translates to "honeybee" or "humming bee" breath, is a humming meditation that can produce a calming effect on your nervous system. This breath creates a vibration in your eardrums that appears to have a nourishing effect on your vagus nerve as measured by an increase in heart rate variability (Nivethitha et al., 2017). The next practice invites you to explore bhramari pranayama for yourself.

# Honeybee Breath

I encourage you to study the effect of this breath practice by noticing how you feel emotionally or by observing changes in your state of mind.

### Orienting and Centering

To begin, find a comfortable seat in a chair or on the floor. Notice your body sensations, your breath, and any emotions that are present for you in this moment. This will serve as a baseline and will allow you to notice subtle changes in how you feel throughout the practice.

### Honeybee Breath

When you feel ready, start by simply exploring how it feels to hum. You might adjust the tone higher or lower. As you explore these various humming sounds, notice where you feel the vibration of the tone in your body. Is this feeling centered in your chest, throat, or face? There is no right or wrong tone.

The goal of this exploration is to find a tone that feels good for you today, and this tone might change over time. You could also explore humming a tune or song that brings up positive feelings or memories. Or you might choose to listen to a favorite piece of music and hum along.

Traditionally, bhramari pranayama involves placing your palms over your ears with your fingers facing down, which will amplify the feeling and sound in your ears. Try this and see if it enhances or detracts from a feeling of connection with your heart. The goal is to cultivate a feeling of sweetness and a sense of connection to your heart, so continue to adapt the practice until it feels good to you. Continue this breath practice for as long as you would like.

## Completion

What are you aware of now as you notice your body, mind, emotions, and level of energy? Take some time to write down any observations, knowing that you can return to this practice as often as you would like.

_____

_____

_____

_____

_____

_____

_____

_____

_____

_____

# Somatic Intelligence

Embodiment is as an active process of self-discovery that you renew and strengthen by repeatedly attending to your sensations, emotions, and movement impulses in the present moment (Fogel, 2009). Mindful body-awareness practices such as yoga can help you build kinesthetic awareness, which is a sense of how your body feels and moves (Price & Hooven, 2018). Often, we think of intelligence as our knowledge of facts, as it is traditionally measured through mental and verbal capacities. However, kinesthetic awareness is a form of somatic intelligence, meaning that paying attention to your felt sense of self provides information that can wisely guide your decisions and actions in the world (Damasio, 1999). The vagus nerve is an essential part of this information highway, and awakening your mind-body connection not only improves your physical health but also enhances your emotional intelligence and capacity to carry this wisdom into your relationships (Hopwood & Schutte, 2017).

Embodiment is best thought of as a combination of input from three sensory feedback systems: exteroception, interoception, and proprioception. *Exteroception* refers to your five senses that help you process what you see, hear, smell, taste, and touch. *Interoception* involves sensory perceptions from inside your body, such as changes in temperature, tension, or pain. These sensations give you feedback about whether you are hungry, thirsty, unwell, or sleepy. In addition, interoception helps you recognize when you are feeling emotions. For example, you might notice a fluttery anxious feeling in your belly, the tension of anger in your chest, or a knot of grief in your throat. *Proprioception* refers to the ability to sense your body in space as related to gravity, which allows you to feel the positioning of your body. Proprioception relies on your vestibular system, which is housed in your inner ear and in the joints of your body. Interoception and proprioception also work together to assist with emotion regulation and attention (Pinna & Edwards, 2020; Khalsa et al., 2018; Payne et al., 2015).

All three of these sensory systems play an essential role in your yoga practice. Exteroception helps you orient to safety and remain grounded in present-moment awareness. Interoception allows you to notice internal cues so you can adapt your practice in response to any physical discomfort or emotional tension. Proprioception helps you feel grounded in your body through the physical experience of the asana. For example, as you explored in mountain pose, proprioception allows you to notice when you are leaning forward, backward, or to one side, which allows you to fine-tune your position until you find a felt sense of your center. In addition, proprioception is essential in all balancing shapes.

As with neuroception, your vagus nerve communicates all of your body's sensory cues to your brain—a process that occurs without conscious awareness. This is beneficial for many reasons. For example, if you touch a hot stove, you will remove your hand immediately without having to think about it first. Similarly, once you learn how to ride a bike, you know how to keep your balance without conscious effort. However, you can also bring conscious awareness to your somatic experience to build your embodied sense of self (Craig, 2010), and in doing so, you are more likely take care of yourself. For example, perhaps you have been sitting in one position for too long and you suddenly become aware that your foot has fallen asleep. Now you can explore a new way of sitting or moving to restore blood flow to this area. In truth, we all have aspects of ourselves that are asleep, sometimes as a way of disconnecting from painful emotions or memories that were once overwhelming. Yoga offers an opportunity to compassionately awaken these parts of yourself that have been hiding beneath the lens of your awareness.

I invite you to think of embodiment as an exploratory journey—one that is an ever-changing, dynamic relationship between you, your circumstances, your relationships, and the world. In other words, how you feel in your body will change depending on many factors, including what you eat, how you sleep, where you are, who you are, and what is happening around you. This is called *intercorporeality*, and it challenges the idea that your embodiment is independent of your surroundings (Merleau-Ponty, 1962; Tanaka, 2015).

How you feel in your body is also a reflection of your relationships with others, and this is especially true in your earliest relationships with the caregivers who shaped your sense of self. As an infant and young child, you needed to be held and touched in a safe and caring manner to nurture your self-awareness and to develop the ability to self-soothe later in life (Jean & Stack, 2009). This is why childhood neglect or abuse can leave a powerful imprint on your physical and emotional sense of self.

Similarly, cultural experiences also influence your felt sense of self (Bennett & Castiglioni, 2004; Kimmel, 2013). If your family, ancestors, and community members respected and empowered you, you might walk through the world feeling confident, with your head held high. However, intergenerational trauma—which involves untreated trauma that is passed down across generations—can impact your posture, gestures, and emotional expressivity (Wolynn, 2016). It can diminish your ability to breathe deeply, move freely, take up space, or use your voice. Importantly, yoga provides a safe space to turn toward these inherited wounds and reclaim a new sense of freedom.

Within the relative safety of your yoga mat, breath and movement practices help increase a felt sense of your body. You can also enhance this self-awareness through touch-based assists, which are common within yoga classes. However, if you have a history of trauma, receiving touch from a yoga teacher might unintentionally trigger traumatic memories. In these cases, it can be more beneficial and predictable to explore self-applied touch as a way to care for yourself during a yoga class. One particular touch practice is self-havening, which involves engaging in self-touch of your face, arms, and hands while reflecting on a stressful or traumatic event (Ruden, 2011). The term *havening* refers to finding a safe haven in the midst of a storm. Self-havening releases serotonin and oxytocin, which can reduce symptoms of anxiety and depression (Thandi et al., 2015). Self-touch combined with self-compassion also provides a tender way of parenting yourself as you care for your most vulnerable feelings (Dreisoerner et al., 2021; Seoane, 2016).

Because the vagus nerve runs through the face, ears, and neck, it can also be quite beneficial to self-massage these areas of your body. However, the idea of self-touch might evoke difficult feelings, especially if your relationship with your body is complicated by a negative body image, feelings of self-loathing, or gender dysphoria, in which you feel a mismatch between your physical body and the felt sense of your own gender identity. Unfortunately, the way yoga is portrayed in the media—often with thin, oversexualized, and able-bodied individuals—can exacerbate this problem and alienate individuals who do not see themselves represented in these images (Razmjou et al., 2017).

If you find that relating to your body brings up difficult beliefs or emotions, try to focus on what your body is capable of doing rather than what it looks like. For example, you might say to yourself, "My body is strong!" or "My body is wise!" Ask yourself what your body needs from you rather than trying to change or control your body. Furthermore, you can enhance embodiment by removing mirrors from your practice space. Every yoga practice offered in this book is meant to be explored slowly enough that you can honor your truth and befriend your body at a pace that feels right for you. Remember, you can skip any practice if you do feel ready to turn your attention to your body.

If it does feel welcoming for you, the following practice provides you with an opportunity to explore the benefits of self-applied touch to cultivate sensory awareness and naturally stimulate your vagus nerve. This practice starts with your head, face, ears, jaw, and neck before moving to your arms, torso, and legs. I like to imagine that you are sequentially waking up each part of the body. Since some of these areas of your body might feel more comfortable for you than others, you are welcome to skip any part of this practice.

# Cultivate Sensory Awareness

This practice offers you an opportunity to explore self-applied touch with various parts of your body, but you can choose to explore only the areas that feel comfortable for you. If at any point you notice distress, practicing dual awareness can help you orient to external cues of safety. You can also adjust the depth of your touch so these movements feel soothing to you. Notice if you have a tendency to want to rush or press too firmly with your fingers. See what happens if you slow down the pace of your movement or lighten the pressure. Although I encourage you to repeat each movement at least two to three times, you might choose to explore some areas for up to a minute. Pause after each touch intervention so you can observe any subtle changes in your body and mind. Follow a pace that feels right for you.

## Orienting and Centering

To begin, find a comfortable seat in a chair or on the floor. Notice your body sensations, your breath, and any emotions that are present for you in this moment. This will serve as a baseline and will allow you to notice subtle changes in how you feel throughout the practice.

## Wake Up Your Hands

I invite you to begin to rub your hands together until you create some warmth in your palms.

## Wake Up Your Scalp

Now bring your hands to your face, and begin to sweep your fingertips along your scalp and hairline, sweeping down toward your ears.

### Wake Up Your Forehead

Sweep your fingertips from the center of your forehead out toward the sides of your face and then gently circle your fingertips over your temples. Now, bring your fingertips to the inside of your eyebrows, at the center of your brow, and create small circular movements here. After several rotations, begin to move outward toward your temples across your eyebrows, and then massage your temples lightly.

### Wake Up Your Cheeks

Bring your fingertips under your eyes near the bridge of your nose and create circular motions across the tops of your cheekbones, moving toward your ears. Lower your hands to place your fingertips beside your nose, just to the outside of each nostril. As you move your fingers away from your nose, you might notice a particularly sensitive area under your cheekbone. This is a lovely place to pause as you create small circular movements here. After several rotations, begin to move outward with circular movements, tracing below your cheekbones toward your ears.

### Wake Up Your Ears

Gently massage your earlobes by rolling the cartilage inward and outward between your thumb and index finger. Locate the tragus of your ear, which is the small area of firm cartilage between your ears and your cheeks. Gently massage this area between your thumb and index finger for about thirty seconds.

### Wake Up Your Jaw

Create circular motions in front of your ears to massage your temporomandibular joint. This area can be tender if you have tightness in your jaw. Bring your fingertips below your earlobes as you continue to massage your jaw with gentle circular motions. You might choose to open and close your jaw a few times as you continue the gentle movement.

## Wake Up Your Neck

Explore massaging the base of your skull by moving your hands behind your ears and interlacing your hands to support the back of your head. Create circular movements with your thumbs, moving from the backs of your ears toward the center of your neck. Then unlock your hands, and gently massage the muscles in the back of your neck by supporting your head in one hand and using the other hand to gently squeeze as you move your hand upward from the base of your neck to the base of your skull. Apply a gentle massage to the left side of your neck with your right hand, and then switch sides to massage the right side of your neck with your left hand.

## Wake Up Your Arms

Massage your left arm with your right hand. Gently squeeze the muscles of your left shoulder, upper arm, forearm, and hand. Move at a pace that supports you to fully experience the benefits of this self-applied touch. Complete this side with sweeping touch as you more rapidly move downward from your shoulder to your hand. Switch sides and massage your right shoulder, upper arm, forearm, and hand. Once again, complete this side with several sweeping movements. Now cross your arms, and place your right hand on top of your left shoulder

and your left hand on top of your right shoulder. Begin to simultaneously sweep both hands from your shoulders down to your opposite hands.

## Wake Up Your Legs

Placing both of your hands on your left leg, create a gentle massage by squeezing the muscles in your upper leg, lower leg, ankle, and foot. Complement this with several sweeping movements across the skin of your left leg. Then switch sides, offering this self-applied touch to your right leg.

## Wake Up Your Back

Explore how it feels to bring your hands to your back as high up as you can reach, and then gently sweep downward across your kidneys and toward the top of your pelvis.

## Wake Up Your Torso

Complete this practice by bringing one hand over your heart and one hand over your belly. Sense the connection between your hands and your body. Remain here as long as you would like.

## Completion

What are you aware of now as you notice your body, mind, emotions, and level of energy? Take some time to write down any observations, knowing that you can return to this practice as often as you would like.

_____

_____

_____

_____

_____

_____

_____

# Eye Movements and Natural Vagus Nerve Stimulation

It is often said that the eyes are the window to the soul. Indeed, your eyes provide great insight into how you are feeling. When you are stressed, you tend to furrow your brow, which contracts the muscles around the eyes, making them appear smaller. When you are tired, your eyelids grow heavy. When you feel connected and excited to see someone, your eyebrows lift, making your eyes appear brighter and larger.

Although you may try to hide how you are feeling by controlling the muscles of your face, you really can't stop your eyes from revealing your true state of mind. This is because the eyes are closely tied to the autonomic nervous system (Mathôt & Van der Stigchel, 2015). For example, when your sympathetic nervous system activates, your pupils dilate to help you scan your environment. This is one reason why individuals who have experienced traumatic events at night are often able to describe the scene as if it was in broad daylight. Similarly, when you feel safe, your eyes tend to sparkle and express warmth as a signal that you are engaging your social engagement system. This is because your vagus nerve connects your eyes to your heart.

Given the connection between the eyes and the nervous system, eye movements have been integrated into many healing practices. For example, eye movement desensitization and reprocessing (EMDR) therapy, which is a form of psychotherapy for trauma, invites clients to move their eyes laterally from side to side as they recall distressing memories (Shapiro, 2018). Our eyes naturally move in this lateral manner as we walk through the world; it is a way of observing our environment. From an evolutionary perspective, this action is necessary for survival, as it allows us to scan the world for food and potential predators. Within EMDR, the lateral eye movements are thought to reduce the fear response in the body and mind and help distance you from the negative emotions related to past traumatic events (Yilmaz Balban et al., 2021; de Voogd et al., 2018).

Eye movements have also been included in many yoga practices. Eye yoga typically involves lowering and lifting your gaze from the tip of your nose to the center of your forehead, moving your eyes back and forth from left to right, and circling your eyes in both directions. Yoga also incorporates use of a single point for your gaze, or *drishti*, to help settle your mind. Given the strain put on the eyes each day—especially if you spend a lot of time looking at your phone or computer screen—it is beneficial to spend some time each day allowing your eyes to rest in total darkness by placing a light eye pillow or resting your palms gently over your eyes (Abel, 2014). By applying this light pressure to the eyeballs, you stimulate the vagus nerve and engage the parasympathetic nervous system.

Given the connection between the eyes and the vagus nerve, one way to achieve natural vagal stimulation is to practice stretching and engaging the eye muscles, which can ultimately help them relax. Your eyes have a direct connection to the suboccipital muscles that sit at the base of your skill, so by moving your eyes, you can release the muscles of your neck to increase blood flow to your vertebral artery, which supplies blood to the brainstem and vagus nerve (Rosenberg, 2017). I invite you to explore these movements for yourself with the next practice, which will guide you through gentle eye movements and neck stretches to nourish your nervous system. If you have a history of glaucoma or other eye concerns, I recommended that you consult with a physician prior to engaging in the eye movements in this practice.

# Nourish Your Nervous System

I encourage you to move slowly with these eye movements and neck stretches, which will allow you to study the subtle effects of these practices.

### Orienting and Centering

To begin, find a comfortable seat in a chair or on the floor. Notice your body sensations, your breath, and any emotions that are present for you in this moment. This will serve as a baseline and will allow you to notice subtle changes in how you feel throughout the practice.

### Eye Movements

If you would like, begin to gently stretch and release the muscles of your eyes by focusing your eyes on a single point that is close in distance. One option is to place your palms in prayer pose about six inches in front of your eyes. Focus your eyes on your fingertips, and after about five to ten breaths, shift your gaze off into the distance, perhaps by looking out a window. Soften your eyes and allow yourself to receive the sights all around you by broadening your visual field of awareness in a panoramic manner. See if you can remain with a widened visual awareness for about five to ten breaths as you notice how you feel in your body.

There is no need to force these movements. Rather, allow your gaze to move between these points as if greeting a long-lost friend with a warm smile. When complete, take a moment to pause and sense your body and breath. If you would like, begin to explore how it feels to bring your eyes to the left and right without turning your head. If you find that you are straining your eyes as you move from side to side, reduce the intensity by finding a smaller range of movement. After about ten sets of eye movements, return your eyes to center. As you complete these movements, notice how you feel in body, mind, and breath.

## Basic Exercise with Eye Movements

If it feels right for you, bring both hands behind your head for support. Gently rest the back of your head into your hands, allowing your hands to provide a little bit of support for your head. While in this position, explore how it feels to bring your gaze toward your right elbow. Stay here for several breaths and observe for subtle cues that your body is relaxing. There is no need to strain your eyes. You might notice an urge to yawn or sigh. Do not worry if you are not experiencing an obvious signal of relaxation. After about ten breaths, bring your gaze back to center. If you would like, rest your arms for a moment and then repeat the process, bringing your gaze toward your left elbow. Then return to center, release your hands, and pause to notice how you feel.

## Forward and Back Neck Release with Eye Movements

Returning both hands to the back of your head for support, explore how it feels to gently stretch your chin upward as you open your elbows wide. If you would like, reach your eyes upward as if looking toward the center of your forehead. After a few breaths, release your hands in front of your face and allow your head to curl forward, cupping your palms over your eyes and supporting the weight of your head. If feels right, allow your eyes to close and rest. Notice how it feels to breathe into the sensations of your upper back, your neck, and the base of your skull. Take your time here, and when you feel ready, slowly lift your head and release your hands.

## Side Neck Release with Eye Movements

This next movement can help release the muscles of the sides of your neck. Start by bringing your right ear toward your right shoulder. You can use your right fingertips to gently support your head while reaching your left hand in the opposite direction to amplify the stretch in the left side of your neck. While in this position, explore how it feels to bring your gaze to the right. Stay here for several breaths, and if you would like, notice how it feels to bring your gaze to the left. Take about thirty seconds to a minute here, and then switch sides to open the right side of your neck. To complete this practice, return your head to center and notice your experience.

## Completion

What are you aware of now as you notice your body, mind, emotions, and level of energy? Take some time to write down any observations, knowing that you can return to this practice as often as you would like.

_____

_____

_____

_____

_____

_____

_____

_____

_____

# Spinal Flexibility and Nervous System Health

We are literally shaped by our life events. How we move, breathe, and hold ourselves all tend to reflect the accumulation of our unique experiences. They provide us with a sense of self. You can imagine the way a child might instinctually curl away from a frightening sound or hide their face from a disturbing image. Or the way someone might intuitively take shallow breaths to protect themselves from feeling vulnerable emotions.

Our posture in particular tends to reflect our emotional and mental state. For example, if you tend to sit with your shoulders slumped, while breathing in a shallow manner and gazing downward, this might be connected to a time when you felt helpless to change your circumstances. Each time you habitually sit in this same posture, you reinforce this experience of yourself (Ogden, 2009). Eventually, you might begin to feel as though this is who you are. However, when you bring conscious and mindful attention to your posture, you awaken to the felt sense of the shape, which allows you to explore new options and create change. Moreover, adjusting your posture can change how you feel emotionally. By lengthening your spine, lifting your gaze, and breathing more fully, you can awaken a new range of emotions, like joy or excitement, and experience increased access to positive memories (Riskind & Gotay, 1982).

Importantly, there is no bad or wrong posture. Just like the various states of your nervous system, different postures provide you with access to different emotions and qualities of yourself. There may be times when curling forward allows you to grieve the loss of a loved one. Other times, you may joyfully lift your face to the sky as you watch a magnificent sunrise. Thus, the goal of therapeutic yoga for trauma is not to always maintain a perfectly aligned spine. In truth, all of us have asymmetrical patterns in our bodies. Our bodies are simply built this way. For example, your heart is nestled into the left side of your chest. As a result, your left lung consists of two lobes, whereas your right lung has three lobes. Likewise, the right side of your diaphragm is larger than the left side, and because your digestive organs are positioned asymmetrically, the right kidney is typically lower than the left. Even the vagus nerve has two vagal branches that innervate the organs differentially.

You might also harbor asymmetries as a result of your unique life circumstances. One of your hips or shoulders might be slightly higher or rotated as compared to the other side. Or perhaps you have experienced injuries or surgeries that impact your use of your limbs. Too often, yoga is taught in a manner that doesn't take into account these natural or accumulated asymmetrical patterns. The cues taught in many traditional classes focus so much on alignment that it can lead a dutiful student to override their body's natural inclinations. In some cases, this process can lead to injuries. Instead of focusing on achieving "perfect" alignment, therapeutic yoga encourages you to view alignment in any yoga pose as a *temporary* experience that gives you access to feelings of strength, empowerment, clarity, or joy that provide a contrast to your habitual postural patterns. This will help you recognize new ways that you might choose to carry yourself in the world.

Polyvagal theory also provides insight into how posture contributes to the health of your body and mind. Many of us have tendencies to tilt the pelvis forward, back, or to the side. It is also common for the head to reach out forward from the body, which places strain on the neck. Spending a lot of time looking at your computer or phone can also exacerbate this forward head position. These common spinal misalignments place strain on the nervous system, which can reduce the health of your body's vital organs.

Therefore, one way to improve your autonomic nervous system functioning is to engage in a variety of yoga practices that focus on enhancing spinal flexibility and correcting common spinal imbalances. Yoga practices often involve moving through postural transitions in a repeated, rhythmic manner that allows you to alternately increase and decrease your heart rate. Because these postures have a strong impact on vagal tone, you can think of this as strengthening the resilience of your nervous system in addition to the physical endurance required in these actions.

The poses in the next practice are not intended to align your body into perfect symmetry but, rather, to facilitate a flexible and resilient spine that will help you respond and adapt to the inevitable challenges of life. I invite you to explore this for yourself in this sequence of exploratory movements that allow you to curl your spine forward, lengthen it back, bend from side to side, and twist in each direction.

# Fluid Movements for a Flexible Spine

This practice initially guides you to move your spine while seated in a chair or cross-legged on the floor, then presents an option to continue this exploration from a standing position.

## Orienting and Centering

To begin, find a comfortable seat in a chair or on the floor. Notice your body sensations, your breath, and any emotions that are present for you in this moment. This will serve as a baseline and will allow you to notice subtle changes in how you feel throughout the practice.

## Seated Spinal Flexion and Extension

Take a moment to notice how you are sitting in your chair or on your yoga mat. Imagine your pelvis as a bowl of water. If your pelvis is tilted forward or back, the water will run over the rim of this bowl. Notice the tone of your spine and whether you feel any natural tendencies for your pelvis to tilt forward or back. Now, I invite you to roll your tailbone back, which will lengthen your torso and lift your chest up. Here you can roll your shoulders back and gently lift your chin. Perhaps you exaggerate the shape by puffing out your chest with a deep inhalation. What do you notice in this shape?

Now, on the exhalation, begin to curl your tailbone forward as you roll your shoulders and bring your gaze down. Once again, exaggerate this rounding of your spine. What emotions or sensations do you notice in this shape? Now, if you would like, begin to move your spine back and forth with your breath, inhaling as you lengthen your spine and exhaling as you curl forward. You might place your hands on your shoulders as you continue to move back and forth, moving with the pace and rhythm of your breath. Open your elbows wide as you lift your spine, and draw your elbows together as you exhale forward.

After about five to ten breath cycles, slowly bring yourself back to center to find an open but supportive posture, lifting the crown of your head so your head feels supported and centered above your spine and core.

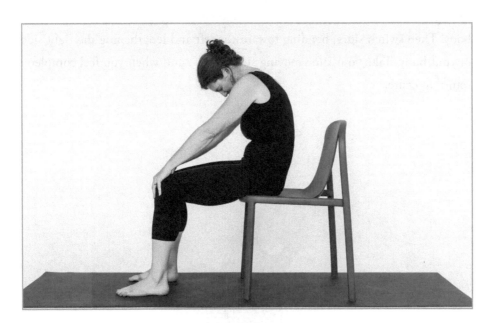

## Seated Side Bend

Now begin to lean your upper body to the right. You can use your right hand against the chair or floor to support your weight. Notice how it feels to contract the right side of your body as you simultaneously lengthen the left side of your body. Then switch sides, bending toward the left and lengthening the right side of your body. Take your time moving side to side, and when you feel complete, return to center.

## Seated Twist

This next set of movements invites a gentle twist to each side of your body. Begin by lifting your arms up above your head and draw your right arm back behind you. You might place your right fingertips on the chair or floor behind you and your left hand on your right knee. Find the range of motion that is right for your body. There is no need to add force into the twist. Honor your body and move slowly and gently.

If it feels comfortable, allow your head to gently turn toward your right shoulder, and if you would like, allow your eyes to move toward the right, gazing behind your right shoulder. It can be lovely to move with your breath by backing out of your twist as you inhale and deepening into the shape as you exhale. Take several breaths here, and when you feel complete on this side, slowly return to center. Pause here for a moment prior to taking your twist to the left. Once again, find a natural and unforced twist while staying connected to your breath.

### Standing Spinal Flexion and Extension

If you would like, you can continue this postural exploration while standing in mountain pose with your arms at your sides. Once again, explore moving your pelvis forward and back. There is a wider range of motion as you explore this while standing. Notice how you feel as you tilt your tailbone forward, which will round your lower back and curl your spine. Allow your neck to curl forward in this shape. Now, notice how you feel as you move in the opposite direction, drawing your tailbone back and arching your spine. See how it feels to draw your shoulders up and back while lifting your gaze. Take your time to explore moving back and forth. Slowly begin to soften the movements so you can explore a subtle rocking of your pelvis. Continue this gentle movement until you find a standing position that feels both supported and open.

## Standing Side Bend

From a standing position, you can bend side to side, allowing your arms to rest by your sides. As you bend to the right, notice how it feels to contract the right side of your body while lengthening the left side. Then switch sides. You might embellish your side-bending experience by lifting your arms overhead and taking hold of the opposite wrist. After several repetitions to each side, return to center and pause to notice how you feel.

## Standing Spinal Twist

You can add a standing spinal twist by drawing your arms up over head. Twist toward the right as you draw your right arm behind you and your left arm in front of you. It is common for your right hip to follow your right shoulder. See if you can resist the twist in your hips by drawing your right hip forward so your pelvis remains even and grounded over your feet. Notice how it feels to twist while staying connected to your center. Return to center for a few breaths prior to exploring this twist on the opposite side.

## Standing Forward Fold

You will complete this standing postural sequence with an opportunity to move between standing in mountain pose to standing in forward fold. Move slowly enough to notice the subtle ways that your nervous system accommodates these transitions. From standing, inhale as you bring your arms up overhead, and exhale as you fold forward over your legs. See if you can keep your knees slightly bent to reduce tension in your lower back or legs. Slowly, inhale as you explore coming to a halfway lift by placing your fingertips on the floor, on your shins, or on blocks in front of you. Then exhale as you return to forward fold. Inhale again and return to standing in mountain pose as you lower your hands by your sides. Take several breaths here and notice how you feel. If you would like, repeat the forward-fold sequence as you mindfully stay connected to your body and breath.

## Completion

When you feel complete, I invite you to take a few minutes to notice how you feel inside after exploring the range of motion in your spine. What are you aware of now as you notice your body, mind, emotions, and level of energy? Take some time to write down any observations, knowing that you can return to this practice as often as you would like.

_____

_____

_____

_____

_____

_____

_____

_____

_____

_____

_____

_____

_____

_____

_____

## Co-regulation, Coherence, and Compassion

During the first several years of life, called the *attachment period*, a child is dependent on the nurturance and protection of caring adults. It is during this crucial developmental period that emotional security is fostered between a caregiver and the infant, which sets the stage for how the child will relate to the world going forward.

You can think of these early attachment relationships as a sort of interpersonal yoga practice—one that creates a sense of union between two people and that forms the core sense of self within the child. A sensitive caregiver attunes to the infant's facial expressions, vocalizations, gestures, and body movements. This attunement guides the caregiver's use of touch, eye contact, and tone of voice, as well as the timing of interactions. Over time, the accumulation of these empathic relational exchanges reinforces our ability to feel connected to our bodies, recognize our emotions, and respond effectively to our needs. In other words, we learn the capacity for self-regulation through *co-regulation*. Co-regulation is when one person's capacity to be in a ventral vagal state offers a calm, compassionate, and regulating presence for another.

Because vagal tone initially develops within the context of these early attachment experiences (Insel, 2000), children who experienced developmental trauma are more likely to have lower vagal tone and corresponding increases in colic, emotion dysregulation, impulsivity, attentional difficulties, and aggression throughout childhood (Beauchaine, 2001). In contrast, children who grow up in a safe, consistent, predictable, trustworthy, and nurturing environment are afforded the ideal conditions from which their social nervous system can develop. Importantly, though, attuned parenting is not meant to be perfect. There will always be a margin of error in which a parent does not meet the needs of their child. Ideally, these ruptures in connection are brief, recognized, and repaired. These "normal" experiences of rupture and repair also serve a purpose by toning the child's nervous system to handle the inevitable stressors of life and to trust that they can be resolved.

However, when a child experiences ongoing disruptions in attachment without repair, they are left in states of profound emotional and physiological dysregulation for extended periods of time—often with caregivers who are dysregulated themselves. Children might become anxious, agitated, restless, or aggressive, which is a sign that they are stuck in a defensive sympathetic nervous system state. However, an infant cannot flee from or fight against a frightening or hurtful caregiver, making them more likely to rely on the defensive actions of the dorsal vagal circuit to survive, which leads them to collapse into immobilization, fall asleep, or dissociate. These early childhood experiences can lead to learned helplessness in which the child no longer believes that their actions will make a difference in the outcome of their life.

One of the costs of traumatic events, especially when they involve relational betrayals, neglect, or abuse, is the loss of trust in human relationships. Connecting with other people might continue to feel unsafe. You might not know whom to trust. Perhaps you remain in relationships with people who are hurtful or unkind even though you want to leave. Maybe you inadvertently push caring people away. Or perhaps your fear of being rejected leads you to avoid seeking any connections at all.

Even if you did not have a nourishing, co-regulating relationship in childhood, it is profoundly healing to have this kind of support and connection in adulthood. Research on neuroplasticity reveals that your brain and body continue to experience changes well into adulthood and that you can continue to develop vagal tone throughout your entire lifespan. While yoga is a deeply personal practice, this path also opens up ample opportunities to practice with others, and this provides additional opportunities for co-regulation when it comes to vagal tone. For example, when members of a choir sing together, they not only harmonize their voices, but also synchronize their breath and vagal tone (Müller & Lindenberger, 2011). Similar actions may occur in yoga classes as students breathe and move together. This harmonious co-regulation increases feelings of cooperation, trust, and compassion (McCraty, 2017).

The neural foundation for co-regulation is compassion, which is distinct from empathy. Whereas empathy often involves feeling someone else's pain, compassion involves witnessing another's suffering without sharing or feeling responsible for their pain (Porges, 2017). Compassion is based on the principle that we respect both the suffering and joy of others, and we honor the other's capacity to experience their own pain. It also rests on the principle that we must start by attending to our own pain and suffering first.

Compassion is not driven by a need to "fix" another person; it offers a calm ventral vagal state that allows us to relate to the pain of others (or the world) without becoming overwhelmed. Although compassion doesn't mean non-action, we choose our actions wisely so we can engage with others in a way that doesn't inadvertently suggest that they are broken or weak. This approach to compassion does not mean that we are aloof or overly detached from others. In contrast, we relate to others and respond in a caring manner without losing a clear and grounded connection to ourselves.

Even when you are unable to connect with others, you can still activate your social engagement system and enhance vagal tone by practicing mindfulness, conscious breathing, and movement. In particular, practices that focus on loving-kindness, gratitude, self-compassion, and forgiveness can all help increase vagal tone, restore the resilience of your nervous system, and improve your overall well-being (Carson et al., 2005; Emmons, 2007; Emmons & McCullough, 2003; Kok & Fredrickson, 2010; Kok et al., 2013; Toussaint et al., 2015). These practices help develop *coherence* within your nervous system, which can be thought of as emotional composure that increases your mental clarity and focus.

When you are in a coherent state, you are better able to make decisions, handle conflicts, and respond to stress. You can better navigate difficult moments by noticing when you feel triggered and, rather than reacting, remember to take a mindful pause. Coherence also allows you to respond to others in a way that is most beneficial. For example, when you are in a coherent state, you can respond calmly and lovingly to a child who is having a tantrum. Likewise, you can learn to hold yourself in this loving way, as if you have become this compassionate, loving parent to yourself. Take some time to explore this for yourself with the following practice, which is focused on self-compassion.

# Self-Compassion

I encourage you to study the effect of this practice by noticing how you feel emotionally throughout the practice and by observing changes in your state of mind.

### Orienting and Centering

To begin, find a comfortable seat in a chair or on the floor. Notice your body sensations, your breath, and any emotions that are present for you in this moment. This will serve as a baseline and will allow you to notice subtle changes in how you feel throughout the practice.

### Reflect on a Difficult Moment

Take some time to reflect on a difficult moment, either one from your past or in your current circumstances. As you reflect on this experience, notice your thoughts, emotions, and body sensations.

### Offer Self-Compassion

Now take a deep breath and see if you can love yourself just as you are. Without judgment, notice if you are able to receive this care from yourself. If you find it difficult to feel kindness toward yourself, see if you can become curious about your experience. What blocks you from receiving this compassion? If you would like, see if you can imagine another person who loves you and treats you with kindness. Notice how you feel as you imagine receiving care and kindness from this person. What emotions are you feeling now? Is it easy or difficult to imagine receiving this care?

You might also imagine another person or a group of people who are experiencing a similar kind of pain or suffering. Explore how it feels to offer this same care and kindness to that person or those people. As you explore offering compassion to others, observe how you feel in your body. Now, return your awareness to yourself and your own need for love and care. Once again, take a deep breath as you explore how it feels to love and care for yourself. You can continue to explore this practice as long as it feels nourishing to you.

## Completion

When you are complete with this meditation practice, take a moment to notice what you are aware of now in your body, mind, emotions, and level of energy. Take some time to write down any observations, knowing that you can return to this practice as often as you would like. If you found this practice challenging, this might be a signal to seek additional support from someone who can offer a supportive and compassionate co-regulating relationship.

_____

_____

_____

_____

_____

_____

_____

_____

_____

_____

_____

_____

## Chapter Review

Within this chapter, you explored yoga from a neurophysiological perspective, looking through the lens of polyvagal theory, which provides a foundation for understanding how and why yoga practices work. You deepened your journey with breath and movement practices aimed to create greater balance in your body and mind. If you would like, take some time to review your written responses to the practices. What are you taking away from this chapter? Are there any new tools that you would like to continue to explore as you move into the next chapter?

_____

_____

_____

_____

_____

_____

_____

_____

_____

_____

_____

_____

_____

_____

_____

CHAPTER 3

•••

# A Journey toward Embodiment: Practices for Mobility and Vitality

Central to healing trauma is having an environment where you can be in relationship to yourself in a very real and authentic manner. You turn toward the felt sense of your body in the here and now and welcome all of your emotions—even the ones you might tend to reject or hide from yourself or others. It is normal to experience anger, fear, and sadness after having experienced trauma, *and* it is common for these emotions to emerge during the healing process. Yoga offers opportunities to get in touch with these raw feelings in a playful manner that allows you to roar like a lion or crouch like a tiger who is ready to pounce. Other times, yoga is the much-needed sacred refuge that allows you to mourn with a soulful cry. So long as you are ready for this process, it is often a tremendous relief when you can finally let go.

All of us are born with hardwired physiological survival instincts that kick into gear when we are facing a frightening event. That means your body will automatically engage in protective responses to anything that you experience as, or even perceive to be, potentially dangerous. Sometimes your body will carry the lingering effects of these stressful or traumatic events even after the event is over. This is more likely to occur if you had no way to protect yourself or escape from the experience. Your body carries these incomplete actions as thwarted instincts—as unresolved urges to fight, flee, faint, or freeze—that become trapped in the body long after the traumatic event is over (Levine, 2010).

For example, if you have an unresolved freeze response, you might notice that you still carry a feeling of being startled or shocked, like a deer in the headlights. Although a freeze response was once necessary for your survival, you might continue to have times when you become excessively still in your body while simultaneously feeling hypervigilant of your surroundings and hyperaware of your body sensations. You might also have a tendency to hold your breath or breathe shallowly. Another term for the freeze response is *attentive and reactive immobility*, meaning that you carry a high level of muscular tone with restricted movement that is driven by your sympathetic nervous system (Kozlowska et al., 2015).

You may also hold traumatic stress in your body as a result of an unresolved flight response, causing you to breathe rapidly into your upper chest or feel restless in your body. As a result, it can be difficult to slow down or connect to your body. The counterpart to this flight response is the fight response, which involves self-protection through kicking, pushing, hitting, scratching, or biting actions. An unresolved fight response can lead you to hold tension in your jaw, arms, hands, hips, or legs. For example, you might notice that you grip your hands into fists or clench your teeth at night. You might find it difficult to relax your body even in safe situations.

Finally, you may hold trauma in your body due to an unresolved faint response, in which case you might be prone to feeling fatigued or disconnected from your body. The faint response tends to show up as a feeling of being collapsed, nauseous, dizzy, foggy, or tired. Although this parasympathetic response was once adaptive for your survival—as it slows down breathing and heart rate in an attempt to conserve energy—this hypoarousal response can return any time you perceive that you are trapped with no way to escape stress. In contrast to the attentive and reactive immobility associated with the freeze response, an unresolved faint response is referred to as *collapsed immobility*, in which the body carries a low level of muscular tone with restricted movement (Kozlowska et al., 2015).

When left unresolved, these patterns of tension and uncomfortable sensations can inform your overall sense of self. Within this chapter, you will have opportunities to energize your body and access the healing power of instinctual movements to help you come out of these lingering patterns of freeze, flight, fight, or faint. You will be introduced to practices that increase your capacity to be present with a wider range of emotions, sensations, and energy in your body. Through the lens of somatic psychology and body-oriented therapies, you will deepen your understanding of polyvagal theory as applied to yoga and explore practices that are aimed to help you move out of your comfort zone and into your growth zone. These practices are designed to enliven your sense of vitality as you stay just a bit longer in challenging shapes. While this might lead you to tap into the discomfort of difficult emotions and sensations, you will also realize that they are temporary. With these practices, my hope is that you can develop a felt sense of your strength and resilience.

## Brain and Body Integration

Trauma has a significant impact on the brain, especially in childhood, when the brain is still undergoing rapid development. In particular, trauma can disrupt neural connections between different areas of the brain, interfering with the brain's ability to integrate information at the cognitive, emotional, and sensorimotor levels. Therefore, crucial in the treatment of trauma are brain-integration strategies, which create healthy neurological connections between the left and right sides of the brain, as well as between the upper and lower brain centers. To better understand this, let's take a closer look at the brain and how its functioning can be compromised by trauma.

Beginning in utero, the brain develops hierarchically from the bottom up and the inside out. The lowest brain structures, such as the brainstem, medulla oblongata, pons, and cerebellum, control your body's vital autonomic nervous system functions, including breathing, digestion, temperature, balance, coordination, and visual orientation. The brainstem is deeply interconnected with the midbrain, or limbic system, which provides the neural basis for memories and emotions. Within the limbic system, brain centers such as the thalamus, hypothalamus, amygdala, and hippocampus work together to help you process and express your own feelings and process the emotions you observe in others. The limbic system also regulates the hypothalamic-pituitary-adrenal (HPA) axis, which serves to mobilize your self-protective defenses through the release of cortisol.

Finally, the most recently evolved structures of the brain are the cerebral cortex and, more specifically, the prefrontal cortex. These upper brain centers help you integrate your present-moment experiences with memories from your past so you can develop an integrated sense of yourself across time. The cerebral cortex is closely interconnected with the thalamus, which receives incoming sensory information from your body that is communicated via the vagus nerve. When you are safe, the thalamus routes this information to your cerebral cortex; however, when you are experiencing stress, the thalamus activates the amygdala, which initiates your stress response systems.

Childhood trauma can have a significant impact on these brain regions by impairing connections between the upper and lower areas of the brain, leading to disruptions in the HPA axis and the autonomic nervous system as a whole. As a result, you might be prone to feeling emotionally hijacked and dysregulated, or you might feel detached and numb. Trauma can also disrupt connections in the corpus callosum, which connects the left and right hemispheres of the brain (Teicher & Samson, 2016). Too much left-brain activity can leave you feeling emotionally cut off and disconnected, while too much right-brain activity can leave you feeling flooded with emotions or painful memories from the past.

In order to restore balance to the nervous system, it is necessary to integrate these parts of the brain so they are once again able to function as a whole. Perhaps the most well-known therapeutic application of brain integration is EMDR, which engages bilateral eye movements to facilitate communications across the left and right hemispheres in a way that mimics rapid eye movement (REM) sleep (Shapiro, 2018; Stickgold, 2002). These rhythmic movements between the left and right sides of the body also appear to stimulate the cerebellum, which creates a felt sense of body-mind integration (Bergmann, 2008; Hannaford, 1995).

Somatic psychotherapies also integrate neuroscience into treatment by recognizing that successful therapy involves a balance of top-down and bottom-up interventions (Ogden et al., 2006; van der Kolk, 2006). Top-down interventions stimulate the upper brain centers through cognitive-based strategies, which often involve teaching you to challenge negative thinking patterns. While these strategies are helpful, they are generally not sufficient because they do not address the physiological imbalances of the autonomic nervous system, which would require working with the brainstem and limbic centers. Bottom-up strategies, which focus on body sensations, movement, and breathing practices, are necessary to engage these lower brain centers. Since bottom-up interventions tend to amplify awareness of trauma-related memories or emotions, you can mix them with top-down interventions to help set a comfortable pace for your journey toward embodiment.

Therapeutic yoga for trauma recovery also offers ample opportunities for brain integration with top-down and bottom-up practices. In yoga, top-down practices can include setting an intention and aligning yourself with self-affirming beliefs, whereas bottom-up practices can include modifying how you breathe, attending to your sensations, moving your body in an empowering manner, or exploring restorative shapes that help you deeply relax. With consistent practice, yoga and meditation can increase your ability to reflect on your emotional reactions and make decisions grounded in logic instead of resorting to automatic survival reactions (Desai et al., 2015; Gotink et al.; 2018; Larrivee & Echarte, 2018; Raffone et al., 2010; Tang et al., 2015). However, you may need to proceed slowly, especially if you are prone to dissociation. Any meditation practice focused on overriding body sensations can reinforce an overreliance on dissociative coping strategies. Therefore, the practices offered in this book emphasize embodiment by attending to sensations at a pace that you can tolerate.

Many yogic practices also facilitate integration through movements that engage the left and right sides of the body. These movements stimulate energetic channels called *nadis*, through which our life force, or *prana*, circulates. The Sanskrit word *nadi* means "little river," which conveys the image of movement along these channels. There are two primary nadis that run along the left and right sides of the spine, which are associated with the states of the autonomic nervous system (Lutz, 2021). The left nadi is called the *ida*, and it is associated with the parasympathetic nervous system, while the right nadi is called the *pingala*, and it is associated with the sympathetic nervous system.

Along the midline is the *sushumna nadi*, often called the central channel, which travels upward from the base of the spine to the top of the head. The word *sushumna* is translated as "easeful or peaceful mind," and this is considered one of the primary goals of yoga. This central channel is associated with the rising of *kundalini*, which is an energetic experience that can sometimes feel like a "spiritual crisis" if it happens too quickly. However, it is much more common that yoga allows you to slowly and mindfully awaken to your own innate power. In this case, the central channel provides an experience of tranquility, balance, and equanimity.

One of the ways that yoga facilitates awareness of the sushumna is through movements and breathing patterns that alternate between the two sides of the body and brain. The following practice offers alternate nostril breathing, or *nadi shodhana*, also known as the channel clearing practice, in which you create an alternating breathing pattern between the left and right nostril to balance the brain and body. This breath practice also has been shown to offer the benefits of increased heart rate variability and improved cardiovascular health (Jovanov, 2005; Saoji et al., 2019; Sharma, et al., 2013).

# Alternate Nostril Breathing

I encourage you to study the effect of this breath practice by noticing how you feel emotionally or by observing changes in your state of mind. This practice engages a slow, smooth breathing pattern. Traditionally, it is done by allowing your left hand to rest gently in your lap while using your right hand to alternately close off each nostril.

## Orienting and Centering

To begin, find a comfortable and supportive seated position in a chair or on a cushion on the floor. I invite you to begin by noticing how you feel right now. Remember, you can take your time with this part of the practice by looking around the room. Notice your sensations, emotions, thoughts, and level of energy.

Before you begin your exploration of alternate nostril breathing, I encourage you to use the thumb of your right hand to block your right nostril. Take three breaths just out of your left nostril and notice the openness of this channel of breath. Do you feel congested? Does this nostril feel open? After three breaths, lift your thumb and close your left nostril instead with your middle or ring finger (whichever feels intuitive and comfortable for you) as you take three breaths out of your right nostril. Once again, notice whether you feel congested or open on this side. This will serve as a baseline and will allow you to notice subtle changes in how you feel throughout the practice.

## Alternate Nostril Breathing

Now begin the alternate nostril breathing. Bring your right thumb back to your right nostril as you take a long and slow inhalation from your left nostril. Next, close your left nostril using your middle or ring finger while gently folding your first or first two fingers toward your palm. This will allow you to slowly exhale out of your right nostril. Keeping your hand in this position, breathe in slowly through your right nostril. Now, switch your hand position again to close off your right nostril, which will allow you to exhale out of your left nostril. This is one complete cycle of alternate nostril breathing. Continue breathing through alternate nostrils for about three minutes or for a length of time that works for you. Traditionally, you will end this practice with an exhalation out of your left nostril.

## Completion

Upon completion of the practice, take several long, slow breaths as you sense the movement of air through both of your nostrils simultaneously. What are you aware of now as you notice your body, mind, emotions, and level of energy? Take some time to write down any observations, knowing that you can return to this practice as often as you would like.

_____

_____

_____

_____

_____

_____

# Yoga at the Edge

It is human nature to seek stability. One way that we do so is by creating habits. In contrast to novel situations—which require more energy because we must devote more awareness to our surroundings—habits simplify our lives and conserve energy. Think about your morning routine. What is the first thing you do upon waking up? What do you typically eat for breakfast? How do you transition into your day? These habits help you manage stress simply because there is comfort in what is known. However, traumatic events interrupt the status quo. You may feel as though the world you once knew has ended. Nothing may feel stable anymore.

At these times, it is important to have tools that help you embrace change. Yoga is one such tool that offers you an island in the sea of change. It helps you focus your attention on your breath while observing your thoughts, emotions, and sensations, allowing you to eventually cultivate the resources needed to turn toward your suffering with compassion. You learn to attend to uncomfortable sensations and painful emotions—to mindfully explore the edges of your comfort zone—which will allow you to grow in a slow and steady manner. From a psychological perspective, this is known as getting to know your *window of tolerance*, which can be thought of as an optimal state of nervous system regulation where you can respond to your emotions and sensations in the most effective manner (Siegel, 1999). Within this zone, you are able to feel connected to yourself while handling the inevitable stressors of life.

Realistically, we all have times when we are metaphorically outside this window. When you're above your window, you feel anxious, panicked, restless, hypervigilant, and overwhelmed. When you're below your window, you feel depressed, helpless to change your circumstances, shut down, numb, or disconnected from your emotions. Initially, your window of tolerance might feel quite restricted, but with practice, you can increase your capacity to remain present with a greater range of emotions and sensations. Yoga helps you widen your window of tolerance, growing your ability to tolerate discomfort and helping you distinguish discomfort from pain.

To stand at the edge in yoga involves deepening into postures just enough so that your mind is compelled to pay attention. If you stand too far back from the edge, you have little to work with, and the practice remains superficial or stagnant. In this case, you might need to engage the yogic discipline of tapas (heat) in order to find the courage to engage with your practice, even if only for five minutes a day. In contrast, if you go too far past your edge, you lose your ability to breathe smoothly, which can lead to injury. In this case, returning to the yogic ethical principle of ahimsa (nonviolence) is a reminder to be kind and patient with yourself and your process.

Every time you engage in a yoga practice, you have an opportunity to check in and notice your body. This allows you to adapt your practice to meet your changing needs. You learn how to fine-tune your nervous system by upregulating or downregulating your practice so you can stay connected to yourself. One day you might discover an edge in a balancing posture, such as tree pose, as you work with a fear of falling. Another day you might explore a longer hold in warrior pose as you breathe into the discomfort of the heat that builds in your legs. If you are someone who is constantly pushing yourself, you might find that your edge involves slowing down and becoming still. How you feel at the beginning of a practice inevitably changes and evolves. Once you have found your edge, you practice being present with whatever arises; this is what allows you to transform and grow.

Stepping out on the edge is often vulnerable, especially when practicing yoga in a group format, which can lead you to feel self-conscious. You might find yourself caught in the need to be seen as perfect, skinny, strong, or intelligent. However, yoga on the edge is really an invitation for us all to join together in this imperfect journey of being human. Ideally, your practice should provide an opportunity to "drop in" and feel your experience from the inside out. You get to show up and learn to lovingly attend to your grief, anger, and joy. You practice living on the edge so you can take the same quality of presence into your daily life. You practice loving yourself in the midst of your tender places so that when you are at the office, with your children, or in line at the grocery store, you can still remember to slow down, breathe, and pay attention.

Of course, we all have moments when we become clouded by self-doubt, fear, or faulty beliefs about our worth based on past wounds. These misalignments block access to our inner witness. In these moments, we might feel as though we are being hijacked by a younger part of ourselves that is seeking our undivided attention. Indeed, we all have younger parts that carry the pain of unresolved events from the past (Schwartz, 1997). In order to heal, we must attend to these parts and treat each one like an honored guest who has an important message that needs to be heard. Ultimately, resolution requires that we listen to and take responsibility for each and every part of us. You learn to be curious. What does this part of you want you to know? What does this part need from you? From a space of acceptance and love, what would you like to say to this part of you?

As you connect to your center—to your inner witness—you learn to bring compassionate attention toward all of the parts that are calling for your attention. By connecting to your center, you cultivate an optimal zone of nervous system arousal that will help you to feel calm, curious, and self-compassionate as you step out onto the edge. Centering doesn't mean that you ignore your distress but that you cultivate this resource so you can turn toward your distress without feeling swallowed by your pain. This allows you to attend lovingly to difficult sensations or emotions, such as irritability, heaviness, sadness, or shame.

Coming out of your comfort zone might feel uncomfortable or awkward, but this is also how we grow. Like a child learning to walk, you fall again and again until you discover the internal engagement of your body that helps you find your balance. New learning and growth are slow and require repetition, but with practice you can learn to get uncomfortable without relying on protective strategies of withdrawal, blame, or aggression. Remember, the purpose of any yoga pose or breath practice is to learn to stay present in the midst of discomfort while trusting that benefit can arise. It is this experience of trust that becomes anchored in your nervous system. In this way, yoga is a training ground for life that will allow you to stay connected to your center while stepping into the unknown.

The next exercise invites you to explore your edge with three breathing practices aimed to generate warmth, stoke your internal fire, and then cool you down. These practices can help you navigate the edges of your window of tolerance by upregulating or downregulating your nervous system. The first of these practices, *ujjayi pranayama*, is a form of resistance breathing that is achieved by creating a slight contraction of the glottis muscles in the throat. This breath pattern is considered warming and energizing for the nervous system and may temporarily increase sympathetic nervous system activation (Lutz, 2021). The second breath practice is *kapalabhati pranayama*, which involves rapid inhalations and exhalations through the nose. Both ujjayi and kapalabhati breath practices produce a temporary stress response with a recovery phase that increases vagal efficiency (Mahour & Verma, 2017; Telles et al., 2011). Finally, the third set of breath practices, *sitali* and *sitkari pranayama*, is associated with parasympathetic dominance and has a cooling effect on the mind and body (Shetty et al., 2017).

The goal of these three practices is to promote greater physiological resilience and autonomic flexibility. Remember that you can pace yourself with every practice in this book by returning to the balancing and centering practices from the previous two chapters.

# Warming and Cooling Breaths

This practice allows you to experiment with three breaths for your body and mind. If you choose to explore these breath practices, start with about thirty seconds to one minute, which will allow you to observe their effects. You can also choose to engage in just some of these breaths.

## Orienting and Centering

To begin, find a comfortable seat in a chair or on the floor and notice your body sensations, your breath, and any emotions that are present for you in this moment. This will serve as a baseline and will allow you to notice subtle changes in how you feel throughout the practice.

## Warming Breath

*Ujjayi pranayama* is often translated as "victorious breath" because the grounding oceanic sound of the breath can assist you to cultivate mastery over the fluctuations of your mind. To begin, I invite you find a comfortable seated position. Take a deep, slow breath through the nose. Exhale long and slow through your mouth with a "haa" sound as if fogging up a mirror. This will naturally create a slight constriction in the back of your throat. This "haa" breath, or *haakara pranayama*, is considered to be a precursor to ujjayi pranayama.

Now, if you would like, close your mouth as you continue to breathe in this manner in and out of your nose. Allow yourself to stay present with the sound of your breath, as this awakens your inner ear. You might begin to notice a sensation of warmth building in your throat or chest. Stay with the breath practice for about thirty seconds or longer if you would like. When you are complete, release the constriction from the throat and take several soft, easy breaths. Take some time to observe and write about the effects of this breath practice.

_____

_____

_____

_____

## Breath of Fire

*Kapalabhati pranayama*, or "breath of fire," is considered to be an energizing and warming breath. Sometimes referred to as a cleansing breath, this pranayama can help clear your mind or uplift your mood. It is recommended that you avoid this breath practice if you are pregnant, are menstruating, or have high blood pressure, asthma, or glaucoma. You can stop breathing in this manner at any time, especially if you experience any pain or dizziness during the practice.

To begin, take a deep breath in and exhale in a short burst as you draw you lower belly toward your spine. It can be helpful to place your hand on your belly, which will allow you to feel the abdominal muscles contract. On the inhalation, release the contraction in your abdomen, which will naturally allow your breath to flow into your lungs. Continue breathing in this manner for about twenty breaths. When you are complete, allow yourself to breathe naturally as you observe the sensations in your body. If you would like, you can repeat this practice one or two more times. When you feel complete, return to a natural breath pattern. Take some time to observe and write about the effects of this breath practice.

_____

_____

_____

_____

## Cooling Breath

*Sitali* and *sitkari pranayama* are considered to be cooling breath patterns for your body and mind. To practice sitali pranayama, curl your tongue lengthwise so it resembles a straw and extend it out of your mouth. Then take a long inhalation through your curled tongue, sensing the cool air moving across your tongue, and exhale slowly through your nose as you withdraw your tongue and close your mouth.

Because of our genetics, not everyone can curl their tongue. In this case, you can experiment with sitkari pranayama, which involves breathing through your mouth while allowing your upper and lower teeth to make gentle contact with each other. To do this practice, bring your upper and lower teeth together while keeping your lips open, and inhale through closed teeth to produce a hissing sound. Then release your teeth and exhale slowly through your nose. With both sitali and sitkari pranayama, see if you can sense the cooling effect of the air moving across your tongue.

Continue this breath pattern for about three minutes or for a length of time that works for you. Then take some time to observe and write about the effects of this breath practice.

_____

_____

_____

_____

### Completion

After completing these three breath practices, take a moment to reflect upon and write about your overall experience of these three breathing patterns.

_____

_____

_____

_____

_____

_____

_____

_____

_____

_____

_____

_____

# Fascia and the Connective Tissue Matrix

When we look closely at the body-mind connection, we recognize that fascia plays a key role in how we physically experience stress or store traumatic events in the body. Fascia, also known as connective tissue, is a fibrous web that extends into every structure and system of your body, allowing the surrounding tissues to slide and glide across each other. For example, there are superficial layers of fascia just under your skin and deeper layers that wrap around your bones and muscles. Fascia also provides a nourishing and lubricating layer around your lungs that intertwines with the pericardium, the layer of fascia around your heart. You can also find fascia in each of your digestive organs and within the glands of your endocrine system, and it is deeply intertwined with the nervous system. In fact, fascia has been described as the largest sensory organ in your body because it houses approximately 250 million nerve endings (Schleip, 2017).

There is a small amount of hardening of the fascia that occurs each night when you sleep, which can be remediated if you move and stretch your body in the morning. However, if you have experienced a physical injury or emotional trauma, you may be more likely to restrict your movement, either as a means of self-protection or as a way to keep vulnerable emotions under the surface. Without movement, this hardening can build up and result in chronic pain conditions, such as systemic inflammation, histamine intolerance, fibromyalgia, and chronic fatigue syndrome. These symptoms of chronic pain then become held in your body as a type of procedural memory. Procedural memories have to do with your felt sense of muscular engagement. Riding a bike or tying your shoes are examples of procedural memories because once you learn these skills, you no longer need to think about them—your brain and body can run this neural circuitry on autopilot.

Furthermore, procedural memories are often resistant to change. For example, chronic pain might start in your body, but it can be maintained by your brain even if the original cause of the pain has been resolved. Since the body is wired for self-protection, these memories of pain serve a purpose in that they attempt to protect you from future threats. However, they can also cause you to experience false alarms in which you contract into pain when there is no danger of injury, or your pain response may be out of proportion to the situation. This can lead to a vicious cycle of chronic pain patterns. For example, if you have a history of migraines or lower back pain, then the slightest headache or twinge in your back can lead to a fear response. You may then think, "I can't handle this," "I will never get better," or "I am powerless!" You may also tense up your muscles or restrict your movement.

However, these thoughts and habitual responses only worsen your symptoms of chronic pain and impede your capacity for natural healing. Instead, you want to engage in healing movements that melt and rehydrate your fascia, prevent the buildup of chronic muscular tension, and increase voluntary control over your muscles. One such type of movement is called *pandiculation*. This involves gently engaging in a full-body stretch and yawning in a way that feels natural and pleasurable. Pandicular movements are the nervous system's way of waking up the sensorimotor system (Hanna, 2004). You can see these movements in animals waking from a slumber, who will naturally stretch and contract the muscles around their spine and legs.

By gently and intuitively stretching your body with pandiculation, you allow yourself to become aware of any tension in your body, which becomes an opportunity to reclaim healing movements that were suppressed, sometimes many years ago (Fogel, 2009). Although you may feel an urge to reject these uncomfortable sensations, there is intelligence in *all* of your emotions and sensations (Pert, 1997). At the same time, you may need to balance attending to discomfort in your body with a focused attention to non-pain-related sensations so you do not become flooded and overwhelmed. In yoga, you practice the art of directing and focusing attention. If pain sensations become overwhelming, you can pace yourself by noticing pleasurable (or neutral) sensations.

I invite you to think of an embodiment practice as a conversation with your body. You listen to your sensations, which allows you to respond with breath and movement. Then you ask your body, "Did I get it right?" Listen for feedback in the form of emotions, changes in sensation, or an overall sense of ease. Notice if you have a tendency to be aggressive with yourself. If you experience a stuck sensation, gently rest your attention there. Ask this part of your body what it needs from you. Allow your curiosity to help you listen more deeply. For example, if you are experiencing tension in your shoulders, explore why you feel this way. You might begin to realize that the tight feeling in your shoulders brings up emotions of sadness, anger, or fear. Breathing into these feelings, you might notice that the sensations change. You might sense a knot in your throat, a heaviness in your chest, or a tightness in your belly. In time, you will naturally begin to soften.

Your breath plays a key role in directing your attention into your body. While your lungs do not extend into your hips or legs, you can imagine breathing into these areas as a way to bring your conscious awareness into these places. This is a powerful practice, especially when you have areas of your body that feel tight, constricted, painful, or numb. Your breath is a signal that you are paying attention. Remember, yoga invites you to create union between your body, breath, mind, and soul. Using intentional breathing, you are creating these connections in a way that helps you tune in to how your body intuitively wants to move out of freeze, flight, fight, or faint. The following practice invites you to explore moving your body in a variety of yoga poses. However, you can move in a natural and intuitive manner while in any yoga posture. In this way, a yoga pose always serves as a foundation for exploratory movement.

# Flow for Your Fascia

This practice guides you through a series of exploratory, natural movements while seated on your yoga mat, from a tabletop position, from a cat-cow posture, and from a downward dog pose. Even if moving your body into these shapes is not available for you, you can choose to explore and receive the benefits of intentional breathing and pandicular movements while seated in a chair.

## Orienting and Centering

To begin, find a comfortable seat in a chair or on the floor. Notice your body sensations, your breath, and any emotions that are present for you in this moment. This will serve as a baseline and will allow you to notice subtle changes in how you feel throughout the practice.

## Intentional Breathing

Take some time to notice if there is a particular area of your body where you are holding tension. For the next few minutes, I invite you to breathe into this area of your body. If needed, use your imagination to send your breath into this area, noticing any sensations that arise. What does this area of your body need? Would it be helpful to place a hand over this area of your body as you breathe? How does this part of your body want to move? Allow yourself to find any intuitive movements that honor your sensations. Continue to breathe into this area of your body. You might notice new sensations in another area of your body. Now you can send your breath here. You might notice emotions. If so, simply allow them to rise to the surface of your awareness, and exhale as you release any physical or emotional tension. Remember, you can take breaks from the practice as needed.

## Cat and Cow

To continue this movement exploration, I invite you to move into a tabletop position on your yoga mat. Take some time to orient to this shape. If you would like, begin to move your spine with your breath. Inhale into cow pose by lifting your tailbone and head to the sky, which will lower your belly. Then exhale into cat pose, lifting your spine and arching your back as you curl your tailbone and head forward. Continue moving back and forth with your breath as it feels right to you. Feel free to pause in flexion or extension of your spine or to change how you are breathing in this shape. Notice how it feels to breathe into the sensations of your body from this shape.

## C-Curve

Now, see how it feels to move your spine side to side, creating a C-curve shape as your tailbone and head move toward each other. You can pause on each side and get creative with this shape. If you would like, you can lift the opposite foot as you curl your spine to the side. Continue moving back and forth as it feels right to you.

## Puppy Dog

From a tabletop shape, see how it feels to reach your hands forward. This will lower your chest to the ground as you keep your hips lifted. You might reach up onto your fingertips, press one hand forward and then the other, or walk your hands from side to side as you open each side of your body. Follow any intuitive movements that feel good to you.

## Downward Facing Dog

Come back into tabletop position, and if you would like, come into a downward dog shape by lifting your knees off the floor and pushing your hips up. You can keep your knees bent for this movement exploration as you find length in your spine. Or maybe you begin to alternately bend and straighten each leg. Once again, allow yourself to be guided by your sensations in this shape.

## Pandicular Movement

You might choose to return to tabletop shape or stay in downward facing dog for this next movement exploration. Begin to find any additional movements that feel intuitive to you. Perhaps you return your awareness to the original area of tension that you began with during this practice. Or maybe you notice that new sensations are at the forefront of your awareness. Imagine that you are your favorite animal just waking up from a nap. Allow yourself to reach and stretch. You might play with making your body small by curling inward and contracting toward your center and then reaching and expanding your shape. You can think of this as a full-body yawn.

Continue to move between contraction and expansion in a way that feels natural and intuitive to you. Honor your rhythms with breath and movement. Allow your movements to come from your innermost knowing. There is no "right" way for you to do this practice. If you notice an area of tension in your body, see what happens if you contract your body toward this area of tightness, and then expand and open with your breath. Is there a shape that feels just right?

Is there a sound that matches the sensation? As if having a conversation with your body, listen to your sensations. What does your body want you to know?

## Completion

Continue this movement journey for as long as you would like. When you feel complete, I invite you to take a few minutes of stillness, resting in a seated position or on your back. When you are ready, notice what you are aware of now in your body, mind, emotions, and level of energy. Take some time to write down any observations, knowing that you can return to this practice as often as you would like.

_____

_____

_____

_____

_____

_____

_____

_____

_____

## The Power of Play

When you experience a stressful event, one way that your body can react is by locking or hyperextending your ankle, knee, or hip joints. In part, this occurs because your body is equipped with the tendon guarding reflex, which engages your hamstrings and calf muscles as a means to protect yourself in the face of danger. This reflex is part of the attentive and reactive immobility associated with the freeze response (Kozlowska et al., 2015). Gripping in these joints is especially common when you feel shocked by an unexpected event. If you carry this rigidity in your muscles, you are more likely to feel numb or disconnected from yourself. In this case, it is important to soften through the joints in your body in order to open up your ability to receive and perceive the world with tenderness.

On the other hand, some people have joints that are hypermobile or too loose. On the surface, hypermobile individuals seem to make great yogis because they are very bendy and can move with apparent ease into backbends or forward bends. However, these individuals need to be extremely cautious in yoga classes because they are more prone to collapsed immobility, in which the body carries a low level of muscular tone. As a result, their joints provide less resistance, which can impair proprioception and reduce sensory feedback, making coordination of movement difficult and increasing susceptibility to anxiety or PTSD symptoms (Bulbena-Cabré & Bulbena, 2018). If you are hypermobile, it is important to focus on muscular engagement while keeping a soft or unlocked position in the joints, especially in the knees, elbows, and wrists.

Since your joints play a key role in proprioception, gentle rotations of your joints can help you feel where your body is in space, develop greater coordination, and maintain balance. On the yoga mat, you support this process by mindfully engaging in movements that release accumulated tension in the joints and muscles of your body while simultaneously engaging enough muscular tone so you do not injure yourself in the process. Moving your joints also helps circulate synovial fluid—a thick liquid that cushions and lubricates the spaces between your bones—which helps deliver nutrients and oxygen your cartilage. However, some styles of yoga encourage vigorous stretching and repetitive movement, which can overtax your joints. Instead, your body is most likely to benefit from forms of yoga that emphasize gentle rotations and unforced movements that help circulate your synovial fluid.

The joints are your body's transitional spaces—transitioning you from one position to the next—which offers a lovely metaphor that invites you to explore the space between the person you know yourself to be and the person you are becoming. You can imagine the way a caterpillar enters the chrysalis and must let go of its old form prior to transforming into a butterfly. Sometimes we hold on to our stories or beliefs, even if they are inaccurate, because they provide us with a sense of self that feels secure. Transitional spaces are an invitation for you to let go of control and to befriend your fears.

As you move your joints in a gentle and unforced manner, you can determine if you are feeling calm and connected, feeling keyed up in fight or flight, feeling frozen, or feeling shut down and collapsed. With this awareness, you can start building tolerance for stress by experimenting with a variety of playful and rotational movements. Indeed, one of the best ways to increase your capacity to handle stress is through the power of play. When you play, you release endorphins. This not only brings joy to life but also temporarily relieves pain. During play, you become so immersed in the moment that you lose a sense of time or feel as though you are in the flow of your life. One of the key aspects of play, including in yoga, is that you also learn to dance with the unknown. Play involves being willing to not know what is going to happen next. It is a willingness to be surprised that helps us to not only tolerate stress but also discover delight, laughter, and joy.

As you practice moving your body in a playful manner, you will experience releases in tension in one area of your body that will inevitably create changes in other areas of your body. That's because the fascia in your body travels along two spiral lines. In particular, there is a band of connective tissue that extends from the base of each side of your skull, across your back to the opposite shoulder, and then around the front of your body to the hip. This fascia line then continues to spiral down the leg to the foot and up again. The spiral pattern is found throughout the natural world in seashells, ferns, flower petals, waves, eddies, and galaxies. Known as the Fibonacci sequence, or the Golden Ratio, this pattern forms the mathematical basis for the sacred geometry that has inspired artists and architects throughout the ages. We find this universal shape elsewhere within the human body, too, such as in the cochlea of the ear and in the double helix of your DNA.

The following playful practice invites you to incorporate this spiral pattern into your joints with a variety of rotational movements. While the initial movements may seem simple, notice how it feels to let go and allow your sensations to guide your movement as you dance with the divine.

# Spiral Movements to Unwind Stress

This practice provides you with an opportunity to explore rotational and spiraling movements in each of the major joints in your body, followed by an invitation for you to find any natural and intuitive movements as you soften into a flowing, free-form dance. If you would like, you might choose to play music for this practice that inspires you to move in a relaxed and playful manner.

### Orienting and Centering

To begin, find a comfortable position either standing on your yoga mat or seated in a chair. Notice your body sensations, your breath, and any emotions that are present for you in this moment. This will serve as a baseline and will allow you to notice subtle changes in how you feel throughout the practice.

### Rotate Your Ankles

When you are ready, I invite you to place your feet hip-width apart. If you are standing, soften through your knees and begin to lift one heel off the ground so that you can rotate around the ankle of that foot. If you would like, you might hold on to the back of a chair for balance. If you are seated, find a position toward the edge of your chair that allows you to rotate around the ankle of one foot. Find five rotations of your foot in one direction and then rotate in the other direction five times. When complete, switch to the other foot and rotate your ankle five times in each direction.

### Rotate Your Knees

If you are standing, it is helpful to step your feet together before you explore the movements in your knees. With your knees bent, begin to create circular movements with both knees at the same time as you circle them in one direction. Once you have completed five rotations, switch the direction of your spiral movements. If you are seated in a chair, lift one foot off the ground, which will allow you to rotate your lower leg in each direction. After five rotations in each direction, switch to the other leg.

## Rotate Your Hips

For your hips, it is helpful to step your feet wider than hip-width apart. Place your hands on your hips and explore moving your hips in five clockwise circles, and then switch directions. You can choose the range of motion that feels right for your body. If you are seated in a chair, you can explore smaller hip circles in each direction to enhance the mobility of your lower spine.

## Undulate Your Spine

As you progress through your body, allow the joints in your spine to move by playing with wave-like undulations in your torso. Moving from your tailbone to the base of your skull, practice waving, bending, and curling your spine. If you are seated in a chair, explore and enjoy these same spinal movements. Initially, this movement might feel awkward. It can help to pretend that you are a snake slithering over sand or a dolphin swimming in the water.

## Rotate Your Shoulders

Next, move to your shoulders and notice what it feels like to rotate your shoulders forward and backward five times in each direction.

## Rotate Your Elbows

Now, bring your attention to your elbows as you lift your arms away from your sides. Then create circular movements with your forearms, moving five times in each direction.

## Rotate Your Wrists

Now, bring the movement to your wrists by rotating your hands five times in each direction.

### Rotate Your Head

If you would like, explore some gentle rotations of your head in each direction. You might begin with semicircles if you have neck sensitivity or a history of injuries to your cervical vertebrae.

### The Spiral Dance

Finally, you have an opportunity to put all of these spiral movements together. Whether you are seated or standing, discover your own dance with the divine and play with rotating your ankles, knees, hips, shoulders, elbows, and wrists. There is no right or wrong way to move. Just go with the flow. Perhaps you add undulating movements through your spine. If you are standing, you might even explore adding a balancing element to your spiral dance by lifting one leg into the air as you rotate around the ankle, knee, or hip of your lifted leg. You might even pretend that you are standing on your own personal high wire in the circus, playfully coming in and out of balance and switching sides when you feel ready.

## Completion

Continue this movement journey for as long as you would like. When you feel complete with your dance, place both feet on the ground and slowly make your way back to stillness. I invite you to take a few minutes of stillness resting in a seated position or on your back. When you are ready, notice what you are aware of now in your body, mind, emotions, and level of energy. Take some time to write down any observations, knowing that you can return to this practice as often as you would like.

_____

_____

_____

_____

_____

_____

_____

_____

_____

_____

_____

_____

_____

# Repatterning Your Body

In somatic or body-centered psychology, we recognize that we can support the healing process by repatterning the body, which involves reclaiming new movement resources that may not have been available to you at the time of the traumatic event. For example, if you felt helpless during the event, you might have a tendency to feel frozen, bound by tension, or collapsed. Yoga offers an opportunity to release these lingering effects of trauma through a variety of movement patterns. For example, you might press firmly into the mat with your arms and legs as you feel the strength of your body, or you might choose to stand up shake your arms and legs. These pushing and shaking actions can help you feel empowered and mobilized in a way that is different from your past. As you release this physical and emotional tension from your body, you can eventually reclaim your capacity for a nourishing relationship to stillness. Once again, you are temporarily engaging your sympathetic nervous system, followed by a mindful pause to allow your nervous system to rest and recover.

Healing movements often feel intuitive. This is because they rely upon neurologically based instincts that are present at birth and provide the foundation for all movements later in life (Bainbridge Cohen, 1994). In particular, we are all born with the same innate reflexes and progress through the same relatively predictable stages of developmental movements as infants. For example, babies have a postural reflex that lifts their head toward an upright position as their body moves in relationship to gravity. This reflex helps organize how the brain integrates information from the vestibular and proprioceptive systems. As a baby gets close to learning how to crawl, they will reflexively experiment with placing their weight onto their hands and knees as a transition between sitting and standing.

Once children can push into their hands and knees, they initially explore *homologous* movements in which the upper body moves independently of the lower body. Often, you'll see babies rocking back and forth at this stage. As they grow, infants begin to differentiate between the two sides of their body as they experiment with *homolateral* movements, which allow them to move the arm and leg on the same side of the body together. Eventually, the child learns to move diagonally across the body, which allows for *contralateral* movements that facilitate communication between the left and right sides of the brain.

Body-mind centering is an embodied approach to movement that identifies a set of key actions that support our progression through these developmental stages. Known as the satisfaction cycle, these key actions involve five phases: yielding, pushing, reaching, grasping, and pulling (Aposhyan, 2007). *Yielding* is best understood as the ability to surrender your weight into gravity, while *pushing* involves lifting onto your hands and knees in preparation for movement. Pushing also allows you to feel where you begin and end in space so you can define your boundaries or protect yourself when necessary. *Reaching* allows you to express your curiosity for the world and connect with others. Finally, *grasping* and *pulling* help you move toward something you want and take hold of that which is important to you. You can imagine the way that this curiosity leads a child to crawl across the room, lift themselves up to standing, and then reach for the loving arms of a parent or grasp and hug a teddy bear. The cycle completes when you return to a yielded state, which allows you to rest and receive the nourishment and positive benefits of what you have taken in, whether this is an object, food, or the loving connection with another person.

Understanding these instinctual patterns provides us with valuable information about how traumatic events can disrupt development. For example, developmental trauma can lead a child to contract in their muscles and joints, and these tension patterns can interfere with their ability to progress through these sequential movement patterns. In some cases, this can disrupt other areas of the child's life, such as the ability to learn cognitive tasks or successfully process their emotions. For example, a child might have low muscular tone that results in poor posture, difficulties with hand-eye coordination, or a tendency toward emotional dysregulation.

Within your own yoga practice, you might notice that these early patterns of freeze, flight, fight, or faint result in tension or difficulty with movement coordination in your body. This self-awareness can help you to have compassion for yourself. Moreover, once you recognize your own somatic and nervous system tendencies, you can work with these patterns on your yoga mat. While most of us do not spend much time on the floor crawling, yoga provides opportunities to revisit these instinctual movement patterns at later phases of our lives. This process can be beneficial in helping us gain physical strength, balance, coordination, dexterity, and breath capacity (Matthews et al., 2016; Niklasson et al., 2015). In addition, these movements can assist in the journey of trauma recovery as you increase your capacity to set boundaries, reach out for support, take in the nourishment of a positive moment, and rest in a restorative manner.

Within the next practice, you have an opportunity to discover yoga postures through a sequence of instinctual shapes that will help you connect to your intuition and facilitate an integrated felt sense of yourself.

# Awaken Instinct and Intuition

This series of postures invites you to explore instinctual movements to help you connect to your intuition as guided by your sensations.

### Orienting and Centering

To begin, find a comfortable seat on your yoga mat and notice your body sensations, your breath, and any emotions that are present for you in this moment. This will serve as a baseline and will allow you to notice subtle changes in how you feel throughout the practice.

### Lion Pose

This pose incorporates an energetic breath aimed to connect you to your instinctual nature. The classic version of this pose is done sitting on your heels with your knees wide, but if this is not comfortable or accessible for your body, you can find a variation sitting cross-legged or on a chair. Allow your arms to extend long as you place the palms of your hands against your knees. Take a deep inhalation through your nose and exhale through your mouth as you stretch open the muscles of your face and make a "haaaah" sound like a lion roaring. Stretch your mouth and tongue as you open your eyes wide and gaze

downward toward the tip of your nose. Open your palms and fingers wide like the sharpened claws of the lion. Allow yourself to get in touch with your inner ferocity! Repeat this breath another two or three times.

## Downward Facing Dog Variation

If you would like, see how it feels to lift your knees off the ground and push your hips into a downward dog shape. Then, keeping your knees bent, bend through your elbows. See how it feels to lower your knees so that they hover just off your mat. Push your hands and feet strongly into your mat. Perhaps bring your gaze forward as if you were about to jump or pounce to the front of your mat. Notice how it feels to tap into your strength in this shape. As an alternative, you can explore a similar shape without as much strain on your wrists by taking your downward facing dog to a wall. Once again, keep a bend in your knees and elbows as you explore how it feels to push strongly through the limbs of your body.

## Lizard Lunge and Dragon Pose

To find lizard lunge, bring your right foot forward into a low lunge position, with your left leg extending behind you and the back of your left thigh extending toward the ceiling. Bring your hands to the inside of your right leg, and take some time here to explore your lunge. You might choose to stay lifted onto your hands, or you can explore how it feels to lower onto one or both of your forearms with or without blocks for support. If you prefer, you can also stay lifted with both of your hands on top of your right thigh. You also have an option to keep your left knee lifted or to lower it to the ground. Notice the subtle differences in this shape if you lift your head and gaze forward and then lower your head and gaze down. You will likely feel sensations in the front of your left hip flexor and psoas muscle. If your left knee has been lifted, you might explore how it feels to lower it and lift your upper body slightly higher by pressing your hands on the ground.

To find dragon pose, stay in this lunge position as you angle your right foot out to the right and twist your upper body toward the right. Allow yourself to find your way into this shape in any way that feels intuitive to you by breathing your way in and out of the lunge and twist. An additional option, if it feels right for you, is to reach back with your right hand and bend your left leg as you "take the dragon's tail" by clasping your left foot or ankle. Take several more breaths as you explore these variations, and when you feel complete, switch to the other side.

### Sphinx Pose

To find this next shape, begin by coming all the way onto your belly. To prepare for this gentle backbend, lengthen and strengthen your legs to protect your lower back. From here, place your elbows under your shoulders so your forearms are on the floor parallel to each other. As you inhale, press into your forearms as you begin to lift your upper body away from the floor. Find a few more breaths in this shape, and then lower your upper body in preparation for the next variation of this pose.

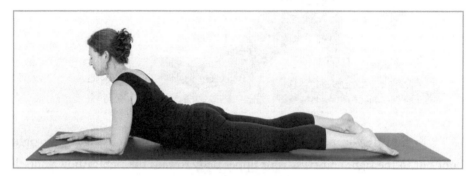

### Half Frog Sphinx

In this variation of sphinx, I invite you to bend your right knee out to your side at a ninety-degree angle. Once again, explore how it feels to lift your torso off the mat with your forearms supporting you. As with lizard, you might explore some subtle variations of this shape. For example, you might explore tucking your left toes under and lifting your left knee off the mat, or you might turn your head and gaze over your right shoulder. You might even press your right hand into the mat as you gently twist toward the right. Alternatively, if this

shape creates too much compression in your lower back, you can find a gentle variation by lowering your upper body closer to the ground or resting your head onto stacked hands. Take several more breaths as you explore these variations, and when you feel complete, switch to the other side.

### Crocodile Pose

The final pose in this sequence invites you to rest and integrate these movements while in crocodile pose. As you continue to rest on your belly, stack your forearms on top of each other, bringing each hand to the opposite elbow, and rest your head down onto your forearms. Adjust your shape until you feel comfortable, and then begin taking long, deep breaths into your belly. You might explore massaging your forehead by gently rocking your head from side to side. You might choose to stay in this shape for a few minutes before slowly pressing into your hands and transitioning back to sitting.

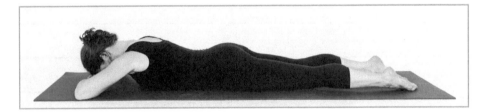

## Completion

I invite you to take a few minutes of stillness resting in a seated position. When you are ready, notice what you are aware of now in your body, mind, emotions, and level of energy. Take some time to write down any observations, knowing that you can return to this practice as often as you would like.

_____

_____

_____

_____

_____

_____

_____

_____

_____

_____

_____

_____

_____

_____

_____

# Embodiment as Empowerment

Many yoga practices build core strength through practices that awaken energy around the navel and create an inner fire in the belly referred to as *agni*, which is the Sanskrit word for fire or the divine spark of life-force energy that lives inside of all people. Agni is the energy in your body related to digestion and assimilation. On a physical level, this is related to how you digest food, so when this energy is out of balance, you are more likely to experience indigestion, bloating, or constipation. However, agni also refers to how we mentally process, break down, and metabolize our life experiences. Unprocessed life experiences can lead to stagnancy, resentment, or mental rumination, but agni can allow you to successfully move past these obstacles. You do so by reflecting on the difficult events, which allows you to discern between what nourishes you and what feels toxic. In turn, you can take the raw material of your life circumstances and turn them into wisdom.

Part of this discernment process involves listening to your gut, which is often called the second brain. That's because your stomach and intestines not only regulate digestion, peristalsis, and elimination, but also produce neurotransmitters in response to your life experiences. Moreover, the vagus nerve communicates these chemical changes to your brain, which explains why our belly brain is referred to as our *gut instinct* in which we feel an intuitive yes or no in response to certain people or situations. You may recall times when you listened to your intuition *and* times when you overrode your gut instinct.

Overriding your gut instinct can also be a habit learned as a result of traumatic events. For example, children who are abused by their caregivers are caught in an impossible situation where they depend on the very person who is also a source of harm. They are faced with a conflict between the need to flee a dangerous environment and the need to attach to their caregivers. With no way to escape the trauma of their household, they need to make the dangerous environment tolerable, which often requires dissociating from the part of themselves that carries the felt experience related to the abuse. In other words, they cut off from their gut instinct in order to maintain the very relationships they need to survive.

This process is often referred to as a fawn response, in which you bypass your own needs—and in some cases, your sense of identity—for the sake of attending to the needs of others. You may also learn to take care of others in order to avoid harm, which is often driven by the false hope that if you take care of them, they will finally take care of you. An unresolved fawn response might lead to patterns of people-pleasing or codependence, in which you continue to sacrifice your own needs for the sake of maintaining relationships.

From a polyvagal perspective, the fawn response suggests a very complex engagement of your autonomic nervous system. First, it reflects an overreliance on the ventral vagal circuit—the social engagement system—for the purpose of appeasing and pleasing others. Second, it reflects an overactive sympathetic nervous system that is hypervigilant in attending to the needs of others. Third, given that the fawn response is often accompanied by a simultaneous reduction in attention to your own needs, it also reflects an engagement of the dorsal vagal circuit in which there is an underlying experience of collapse or helplessness in that you will never get your needs met.

Yoga offers tools to help you overcome these obstacles of powerlessness. I invite you to think of an obstacle as anything that stands in the way of you feeling fine, free, or at ease. Through yoga, you can connect to your inner fire, which helps you tap into a felt sense of courage to turn toward difficult emotions and sensations. Rather than collapsing into powerlessness, you can find a felt sense of strength in your body that provides a contrast to those experiences of relational loss, confusion, or powerlessness. Your core strength in particular can be thought of as a tether to your center.

Within the qigong tradition, the *dantian* (which sits about two inches below your navel) is considered to be a source of stability. Your center serves as a safe harbor in the stormy moments of life. Ultimately, connecting to your core will support you to open your heart to others and the world without losing a connection to yourself. While many of the practices in this book will help you access your inner source of strength, this next series of movements and postures is specifically aimed at helping you awaken agni by connecting to your core with rhythmic cross-lateral movements to facilitate brain and body integration.

# Connect to Your Core

This practice is focused on developing a connection to your core through rhythmic movements between the left and right sides of the body. If you would like, you can focus this practice by setting an intention to work through a specific obstacle that you are facing at this time.

## Orienting and Centering

To begin, find a comfortable seated position on your yoga mat. If you would like, place one or both hands over your belly, and take several long, deep breaths into the core of your being. Take a moment to commit to yourself. Remember that your body is your best yoga teacher. Listening to your gut wisdom is essential within this and all practices.

## Focus Your Intention

As you deepen your awareness of your body and mind, take a few moments to notice if you are experiencing any specific challenges physically, emotionally, or mentally. Do you notice any areas of tension or holding in your body? Are there any places where your breath does not flow easily? Are you carrying any emotional heaviness or stagnancy? Do you notice that you are worrying about the future or ruminating about the past? I invite you to set an intention to work with this obstacle during this practice and allow your breath, movement, and body awareness to help you see the path forward with greater clarity.

## Boat Pose

From here, notice how it feels to place your feet out in front of you on the mat to explore boat pose. With your hands behind your knees to begin, slowly move your torso back and away from your legs. Continue to feel a strong connection to your core as you lengthen your spine in this shape. You might choose to balance by lifting your feet off the ground and bringing your shins parallel to the ground. You might experiment with allowing your arms to lengthen along the sides of your legs as you balance in this shape. See how it feels to stay here for about five to ten breath cycles, knowing that you can lower your feet to the ground at any point.

### Supine Cross-Crawl

This next shape is explored from your back. If you would like, lower your back down onto your mat, and take a moment to breathe with the soles of your feet on the ground and your hands over your belly. To prepare for cross-crawls, I invite you to place your hands behind your head and to lift your feet off the ground. Slowly and mindfully inhale and then exhale as you twist and bring your right elbow to your left knee. Inhale to center and then exhale as you twist and bring your left elbow to your right knee. Continue to move slowly and mindfully from side to side until you have completed about five to ten repetitions of this movement.

When you feel complete, lower your upper body and feet down to the ground and return your hands to your belly. If you would like, repeat a second round of five to ten repetitions of supine cross-crawls. As a transition to the next shape, I invite you to bring your knees toward your chest and wrap your hands behind your knees. If it feels all right, take several rocking motions back and forth along your spine until you rock all the way up and over into a tabletop position.

### Tabletop Cross-Crawl

From a tabletop position, bring your right leg off the ground so that it is extended straight behind you. If needed, you can place a folded blanket under your left knee to reduce discomfort. Take a moment to find your balance in this shape. If it feels accessible, lift your left hand off the floor and extend your arm out in front of you. Once again, take a moment to find your balance. Now, if you would like, exhale as you draw your right knee and left elbow toward each other under your body and curl your spine. Inhale as you re-extend your arm

and leg. Continue moving between these two shapes with your breath for about five more breath cycles before repeating on the other side.

## Standing Cross-Crawl

Now you have an opportunity to explore the cross-crawl movements in a standing position. Begin in mountain pose with your feet hip-width apart, and

slowly and mindfully begin to shift your balance into your right leg as you bend your left knee and lift your left foot off the ground. Simultaneously, begin to bend through your right elbow to cross toward your left knee. Slowly and mindfully return your foot to the ground, and switch sides as you lift your right knee and lower your left elbow across your body. Continue moving in a rhythmic manner four or five more times.

## Eagle Pose

The final pose in this sequence invites you to cross midline several times. The position of the arms typically blocks your vision, so you will need to rely on your other senses, such as the sound of your breath and proprioception, to help you balance in this shape. You will also benefit from engaging the core and hugging everything into midline. This balancing pose can also be done sitting in a chair by crossing one leg over the opposite and crossing your arms. To find eagle pose, create a gentle bend in your knees and begin to balance on your left leg as you lift your right leg off the floor and cross your right thigh over your left thigh. You can find a single wrap of the legs, which can allow you to use your left toes as a kickstand, or you might play with a double wrap by tucking your right toes behind your left calf.

When you feel ready and balanced, open your arms wide like wings of a bird, and slowly cross your arms in front of your body with your right arm underneath your left arm. You have an option to stay with a single crossing of the arms by taking your hands to opposite shoulders. Or, if it is accessible in your body, cross your right hand behind your left forearm, which might allow you to press your right hand into your left palm. Lifting your arms in this shape will bring them in front of your eyes.

As you explore this shape, I invite you to bring your initial intention and obstacle back into your awareness. What helps you trust yourself when you cannot clearly see the path forward? Take several breaths in this shape, and when you are ready, switch sides.

## Completion

When you feel complete, come back to standing with your feet beneath your hips. I invite you to take a few minutes of stillness resting in a seated position or on your back. When you are ready, notice what you are aware of now in your body, mind, emotions, and level of energy. Allow yourself to reflect on the challenge or obstacle that you are facing and the intention that you identified at the beginning of this practice. Are you aware of any changes within you or insights about this area of difficulty? Take some time to write down any observations, knowing that you can return to this practice as often as you would like.

_____

_____

_____

_____

_____

_____

_____

_____

_____

_____

_____

_____

_____

_____

_____

_____

_____

_____

# Enhance Your Vitality

When you experience a frightening or stressful event, your body releases cortisol into the bloodstream, which initiates the fight-or-flight response and mobilizes your body to respond to the threat at hand. Ideally, you are able to respond with some kind of movement during this state of mobilization that allows you to release this surge of energy. Many wild animals will shake as a way to discharge adrenaline after escaping a dangerous or life-threatening event. This shaking allows the nervous system to return to homeostasis and the cortisol levels to return to baseline. Likewise, we see this instinctual propensity to shake in young children after exposure to a frightening event, as they tend to be less inhibited than adults (Berceli, 2015).

However, many adults suppress this natural tremoring response because they do not have sufficient support or a safe enough space to allow for an emotional and somatic release. When this movement or shaking doesn't occur, we are more likely to remain in a state of attentive and reactive immobility or collapsed immobility because the body has not discharged the stress or reclaimed a sense of resolution. In turn, stress can remain stored in the body for many years, leading us to develop somatic "armoring" or "holding patterns." Left unresolved, these somatic patterns can have consequences on your physical health, leading to headaches, digestive problems, or chronic pain.

Although defensive holding patterns can be held anywhere in your body—including in your forehead, jaw, neck, chest, diaphragm, stomach, or hips—they are typically maintained through contractions in the psoas and hip flexor muscles. In part, this is because these muscles help prepare your body to fight or flee by drawing your knee in toward your abdomen in preparation for running or kicking movements. In addition, when faced with a frightening event, many people draw their knees toward their chest as an instinctive urge to curl into a fetal position, which also protects the vital organs. When we maintain tension in the large muscles of the legs, such as the quadriceps, hamstrings, and inner thighs, we also tend to carry tension in the psoas.

Although you might be able to recall specific events that led to these somatic patterns, if these patterns began prior to age five, you might not have any clear understanding of the triggering events. Sometimes these somatic patterns are also related to intergenerational trauma that has been passed down to you. For example, your parents or grandparents might have unprocessed trauma that was carried in their bodies, especially if they had experiences of being exiled, oppressed, displaced, enslaved, or annihilated (Menakem, 2017). These legacy wounds are then passed down in the form of genetic changes that affect how we respond to stress (Wolynn, 2016).

In addition to intergenerational trauma, collective traumatic events can impact your body, mind, and soul. Collective trauma refers to the impact of events that are experienced by groups of people, communities, or society as a whole. For example, even if your direct ancestors were not enslaved, the collective experience of living as a Black person in America shapes how you move, breathe, and carry yourself in the world. In addition, the COVID-19 pandemic is a collective trauma that has impacted millions around the world. Likewise, climate change has a global impact. Healing from collective trauma involves recognizing that we are not alone in our grief or our need find a meaningful path forward. Having a yoga practice amid challenging times can be grounding and can also help us feel empowered to take meaningful actions in a changing world.

Healing from trauma asks you to become a courageous witness of these wounds, whether they are personal, transgenerational, or collective. Although you can cultivate this courageous witness within you for yourself, most people benefit from having the experience of being witnessed by another who is willing to hold space for them. That's because witnessing a wound is a sacred task that requires you to stay present with emotions that have an energetic intensity, including rage, disgust, fear, collapse, and despair. To stay present with the intensity of this experience, you must be able to tolerate feeling the energetic charge of these big emotions without losing a connection to your center. You must learn how to stay grounded in the midst of the storm.

Within somatic psychology, *grounding* is a term that refers to your ability to sense your body and orient to the present moment even in the midst of challenge. The experience of grounding is facilitated by your proprioceptive system, which supports your ability to sense where you are in space. Often, grounding is accomplished by feeling the connection between your body and the earth. You can use weighted blankets to amplify these sensations or practice grounding outside by placing your bare feet down on the earth. Once you are grounded, energy flows from your body down into the earth, which helps establish a sense of safety and centeredness, even when holding space for big, intense emotions.

Alexander Lowen, who developed bioenergetics, first introduced the concept of grounding. He recognized that one of the ways that people push away painful memories is by avoiding the sensory experience of their body (Lowen, 1977). It is as if they are trying to resist the pull of gravity—because if they were to really feel their body, they would feel the *gravitas* or heaviness of the pain. You can better understand this concept by imagining how a child will release their weight into the comforting arms of a caregiver when they feel safe. In contrast, a child who feels threatened will engage their defenses and tense their muscles as a means of self-protection. This muscular tension is a way of pushing away a felt sense of an unsafe environment. As this child continues to develop, these patterns of tension can impact how they crawl and walk.

Postures that fatigue the leg muscles tend to induce tremoring or shaking, which allows the psoas and leg muscles to release accumulated tension. Within bioenergetics, this is accomplished through a series of physical postures that facilitate grounding—such as a squat, standing arch position, and forward fold—that both strengthen the legs and release built-up tension from the body. You can find similar postures within David Berceli's Tension and Trauma Releasing Exercises (TRE®), which is a body-based technique that encourages therapeutic tremoring to release muscle tension and reduce anxiety (Berceli, 2008). There are also parallels between bioenergetics, TRE, and yoga postures, such as chair pose, yogi squat, standing supported backbend, rag doll forward fold, bridge pose, and reclining bound angle pose.

While bioenergetics and TRE focus on releasing trauma through postures that encourage tremors, this process is not for everyone. As with any embodiment practice, grounding can sometimes bring difficult emotions to the surface. It is important to listen to your body and recognize the healing rhythms that support your growth. If you notice that your body does begin to spontaneously tremor or shake during your yoga practice, then you can explore whether you would like to enhance these movements or slow them down. You are in charge of this process. Coming out of patterns of freeze, fight, flight, or faint needs to occur at a pace that you can tolerate. Letting go of tension can be difficult and can feel like a loss of control. To build your capacity for this vulnerable process, you can begin by actively engaging the muscles of your legs. Initially, focus on feeling your strength so that, in your own right time, you can eventually let go.

The following practice offers a series of postures aimed to facilitate an active, grounded, and empowered feeling within your yoga practice. These postures might naturally evoke shaking in your legs and lower belly, but there is absolutely no need to make these tremors happen. The final two postures also have a restorative variation that allow you soften and relax as you rest into the support of your yoga mat. Remember, there is no need to rush your healing journey. Trust yourself and your body.

# Grounding Flow

This sequence of yoga postures focuses on grounding by awakening your sensations in your legs and lower body. The final postures offer an opportunity for you to let go of tension and release your weight into gravity. As with all of the postures offered in this book, explore the variations that work in your body while honoring the fact that you may need to build up to these shapes and revisit them when the time is right for you. To support your practice, you may also find it helpful to have two blocks for these poses.

## Orienting and Centering

To begin, find a standing position on your yoga mat. I invite you to begin by noticing how you feel right now. This will serve as a baseline and will allow you to notice subtle changes in how you feel throughout the practice.

## Chair Pose

With your feet hip-width apart, firmly ground both feet into the mat while you bend both knees as if sitting into a chair. This will engage the muscles of your legs. Simultaneously find a sense of lift as you lengthen through your torso and draw both arms up in front of you or overhead. You can find a variation of this shape by pressing into a squat with your back supported against a wall. Another option is to use a chair underneath you and to build your strength by slowly lifting away from the chair and returning to a seated position.

In whichever variation you have chosen, notice how it feels to remain rooted into the earth. Take your time in this shape to breathe and notice your internal experience. See if you can stay for at least five deep breaths or, if you'd like, explore how it feels to stay in the shape long enough to allow some heat to build in your legs. Notice if your mind begins to wander. If it feels right to you, explore staying for at least one more breath as you invite your attention back to your body. When you feel complete, press into your feet to return to a standing shape with your arms by your sides.

## Yogi Squat to Five-Pointed Star

Yogi squat gives you an opportunity to root into your hips. Come into this shape by stepping your feet wide enough to lower your hips. You can choose the depth of this squat, which might involve bringing your hips to the same height as your knees or closer to your heels. An alternative is to hover your hips just above a chair and revisit the hovering chair pose from the previous posture. Your toes and knees should face the same direction to protect your knees. Listen to your body. You might need to sit on a block or place a folded blanket under your feet to support yourself in this posture. In addition, you can adjust the depth of your hips in this pose to find a shape that works for you.

Once you have found your shape, press your elbows into your legs, which will help lengthen your spine and lift your heart. See if you can stay for at least five deep breaths or longer if you'd like. Can you find just a little more ease in this intense shape? When you feel ready, press into your feet to rise up into a five-pointed star shape, keeping your legs in a wide stance and extending your arms out to each side. If you would like, I invite you to repeat both of these shapes two more times, sensing your strength.

## Standing Supported Backbend

For this shape, you can choose to stand with your feet hip-width apart or wider. To begin, place your palms onto your lower back with your fingers pointed up or down. Your hands will help you press your pelvis slightly forward. Create a soft bend in your knees to avoid hyperextension. From here, press downward through your feet as you begin to lift and arch your torso upward. You can keep your chin tucked or slightly lifted, depending on what feels comfortable in your neck. Remember to breathe into your belly. Explore your edge in this shape. Some discomfort is normal, but you do not want to experience any pain in you lower back. You may notice that the muscles in your legs begin to grow tired in this shape. See if you can stay for at least five deep breaths or longer if you'd like. When you are ready, return to standing.

## Ragdoll Forward Fold

Stand with your feet hip-width apart, and keep your knees bent as you lower your torso over your legs. You can allow your hands to dangle down toward the floor for support, or you might choose to bring each hand into the crease of the opposite elbow. If you prefer, you can choose a chair-based variation of this pose. Explore how it feels to press into your feet as you lift your hips, but keep a slight bend in your knees. If you are standing, you might notice a slight trembling in your legs in this shape. You can always lift up out of the shape at any time, which will stop the shaking. If you choose, you might remain here for several more breaths. When you feel ready, press into your feet and slowly roll up to standing.

## Bridge Pose

Bridge pose is a shape that can be active or restorative, depending on how you approach the posture. It is important to not turn your head in this shape. If you have a history of injury in your neck, I recommend that you avoid this posture unless you are working directly with a yoga instructor who can help you adapt this shape for your body. This shape begins by lying on your back on your yoga mat with your knees bent and your feet planted firmly into the ground. From here, press into your feet to lift your hips and lower back off the floor.

For an energizing version of this shape, you might clasp your hands below your lower back and press into your arms to lift your hips higher. If you would like a more restorative version of this posture, you can choose to place a block underneath your sacrum and rest in a supported bridge. In either version of this shape, you can choose to stay as long as you would like, and when you are ready, release your hands or the block and lower your spine and hips to the floor. Once you arrive, take a few moments to extend your legs long and receive your experience of this posture.

### Reclined Bound Angle Pose

The final shape in this sequence of postures releases tension from the psoas, hip, and leg muscles. To enter into this shape, lie down on your back on your yoga mat, with your arms resting by your sides, and bend your knees to bring the soles of your feet together. You can experiment with moving your feet farther away from your body or bringing them in closer to you, depending on what feels comfortable to you. Once again, you have choices about how you would like to approach this shape. The restorative version is to place blocks underneath your knees at any height that feels right to you. Or, if you prefer, you can explore this shape without blocks.

Initially, you might allow your knees to release into gravity, but you also have the option to slowly lift your knees just an inch closer to each other. Pause here and notice any subtle sensations in your body. Once again, you might choose to lift your knees one inch higher up. It is possible that you will notice shaking or tremoring in your legs or lower belly. If at any point this shaking is uncomfortable, you can simply lengthen both legs, which will stop the tremoring. Once again, you can stay with this process for as long as you would like. I encourage you to find the supported and restorative version of this shape with or without the blocks for a few breaths before leaving this shape. Take a few moments to extend your legs long and receive your experience of this posture.

## Completion

To complete this practice, you can choose to remain lying on your back or return to a seated position. When you are ready, notice what you are aware of now in your body, mind, emotions, and level of energy. Take some time to write down any observations, knowing that you can return to this practice as often as you would like.

_____

_____

_____

_____

_____

_____

_____

## Chapter Review

Within this chapter, you explored how somatic psychology and body-oriented therapies can be brought into yoga. The practices in this chapter focused on instinctual movements that can help you come out of lingering patterns of freeze, flight, fight, or faint. You had an opportunity to meet your edge with specific practices aimed to enhance your vitality. Take some time to review your written responses to the practices. What are you taking away from this chapter? Are there any new tools that you would like to continue to explore as you move into the next chapter?

_____

_____

_____

_____

_____

_____

_____

_____

_____

_____

_____

_____

_____

_____

_____

## CHAPTER 4

# The Strength to Surrender: Practices for Realization and Relaxation

The yogic path ultimately invites you to embark on a spiritual quest for self-realization. Through your commitment to practice, you accumulate a reservoir of embodied wisdom that resides within you. You develop greater capacity to rest in feelings of calm and ease. These moments tend to serve as a reset that offers deep nourishment for your body and mind. They also tend to inspire you to show up in the world with greater authenticity, kindness, and warmth.

From a Western, psychological perspective, self-realization is similar to Abraham Maslow's (1968) concept of self-actualization, which is a state of complete personal fulfillment. When you are self-actualized, you are open-minded and have a greater capacity to cope with uncertainty and challenge. In this state, you become more loving toward yourself and others. Not only can this enhance your compassion, but it also tends to increase your desire to find meaningful actions in the world. You identify as part of a larger, collective whole and are drawn to serve a cause that is greater than yourself. While unwanted and painful life experiences may shape who you are, you also have the power within you to grow and to create a meaningful and purposeful life.

The previous chapters have prepared you to achieve this state of self-realization by helping you release defensive bracing or vigilance from your body and mind. You have practiced coming out of freeze or collapse into the presence of a balanced and regulated nervous system. This chapter focuses on helping you connect to the subtle aspects of the yoga practice so you can cultivate a sense of peace and awaken to the essence of who you are. Toward this end, you will explore a loving-kindness meditation, mindful flowing movements, heart openers, and hip openers. You will also have an opportunity to discover the gift of settling into stillness as you nourish your nervous system through restorative practices. I invite you to approach these practices with a beginner's mind, which recognizes that even the simplest practice offers opportunities for new insight.

The physical postures (asana) and breathwork (pranayama) in these practices will prepare your body for meditation (dhyana). From a yogic perspective, meditation is not meant to be an effortful experience. Rather, it is a natural outcome of all the previous practices that is often felt as a spontaneous opening of the heart. Thus, meditation is not an action; it is a receptive state of awareness. This inward turn is the invitation for you to come home to yourself. You build the capacity for this state each time you practice redirecting your attention away from the outer world. Meditation involves letting go and surrendering to your own presence in stillness.

## A Path to Self-Realization

Yoga postures, breath practices, and meditation help you awaken to the essence of who you really are. You move past your physical armor, emotional tension, and mental activity as you make your way into the very center of your being. These layers of the self are referred to as the *koshas*, which translates as "sheaths of consciousness." The first layer is your physical body, which is called the *annamaya kosha*. You refine the health of this layer through asana, which nourishes your digestive system, balances your endocrine system, flushes out stagnant lymphatic fluid, and replenishes your entire body with freshly oxygenated blood.

The second layer is the *pranamaya kosha*, which houses your breath and emotions. Traumatic events tend to have a significant impact on the way you breathe, often causing you to hold your breath in order to avoid feeling your emotions, but by practicing conscious breathing, you can get in touch with your sadness, hurt, resentment, or anger. Releasing these emotions is how you enhance the health of this aspect of self.

The third layer of the self is the *manomaya kosha*, which is associated with your mind and your thoughts. The tendency of the human mind is to analyze the world. While this allows you to discriminate between things, it can also lead you to see them as separate parts, which can inhibit your capacity to connect to the heart. Yoga facilitates the inward turn of meditation to work through this layer of consciousness. The goal is to drop below the chatter of the mind. Just like the surface of the ocean, your thoughts can sometimes be turbulent and choppy. While you cannot fully stop yourself from thinking, it is possible to drop below the surface. Even though there may be winds stirring up waves above, down in the depths of the ocean is a great stillness.

In learning to anchor your awareness in this stillness that resides within you, you can observe the fluctuations of your mind and emotions without losing access to this inner calm. This inner calm is the fourth layer, called the *vijnanamaya kosha*, which is the seat of your intuition. This layer represents a connection to a quiet yet powerful sense of yourself. The traumatic events of your life might lead you to forget that you have this inner knowing inside of you. However, this intelligence is always here for you and, in time, you can restore a connection to your intuitive guidance, which will help you navigate the challenges of the world with greater confidence.

The final layer is the *anandamaya kosha*, which is described as the bliss body or the light of pure consciousness. Here, there is no duality of body and mind. Rather, this layer of consciousness resides in the very center of your heart. This is an experience of peace felt in the space between your thoughts and the pause between your inhalation and exhalation. A taste of this felt experience provides clarity and helps you see yourself and others with greater compassion. This reflects the state of self-realization, and it allows you to see the beauty and light in other people and all life. This oneness or experience of union is the very essence of yoga.

One practice that supports this journey to the heart is a loving-kindness meditation, which focuses on sending warmth, friendliness, and goodwill to yourself and others. A loving-kindness meditation invites you to turn toward your suffering by wishing yourself well. You can then choose to extend the practice to others, even to those who have been a source of difficulty in your life. Engaging in a loving-kindness meditation may not feel accessible at first. If you are highly self-critical, it is more likely that you will feel uncomfortable or even somewhat threatened by this practice. If you have a history where someone who was supposed to care for you was also a source of threat, bringing kindness toward yourself might evoke grief, shame, or distrust. You might find it difficult to access or sustain positive emotions. It might also bring up habitual beliefs, such as "I don't deserve love" or "I am unworthy."

However, the goal of this practice is not to eradicate these difficult feelings or beliefs. Instead, you are bringing your pain to the surface of your awareness in order to be healed. You are working through the layers of consciousness, or koshas, so you can release these lingering blocks to your aliveness. Once you are aware of these blocks, you will be better able to attend to and heal these wounds. In his book *No Mud, No Lotus*, Buddhist teacher Thich Nhat Hanh (2014) describes how the lotus flower must have its roots in the mud in order to bloom. He offers this metaphor as a reminder that in order to find happiness, you must work through your wounds from the past, as muddy as they might be. Rather than bypassing your pain, your growth relies on your ability to compassionately attend to your suffering. This is the practice that opens your spiritual heart.

A trauma-informed approach to loving-kindness invites you to be flexible with this next practice. Whereas this meditation traditionally begins by extending loving-kindness to yourself, this may not feel like the right place to start if doing so evokes too many difficult emotions. Therefore, you might choose to begin practicing loving-kindness for another person. In doing so, try to find someone who evokes feelings of warmth and compassion naturally and without too much effort. From here, you might explore sending loving-kindness to yourself, a neutral person, or a difficult person in your life. Sending loving-kindness to a person who has harmed you is never a requirement. Every practice begins with choice.

# Loving-Kindness Meditation

This practice invites you to explore a loving-kindness meditation. You can adapt this meditation by changing the order or doing only a portion of the practice.

## Orienting and Centering

To begin, find a comfortable seat in a chair or on the floor. Notice your body sensations, your breath, and any emotions that are present for you in this moment. This will serve as a baseline and will allow you to notice subtle changes in how you feel throughout the practice.

## Loving-Kindness for Yourself

A loving-kindness meditation involves a set of phrases that you repeat silently or quietly to yourself. When you feel ready, explore how you feel as you say to yourself:

> May I be well.
> May I be kind to myself.
> May I be safe from harm.
> May I be peaceful and at ease.

As you say these words, notice how you feel in your body. So long as the practice feels nourishing to you, repeat these phrases several more times, allowing the positive feeling of warmth to grow. If for any reason you feel grief, shame, hurt, or self-criticism during the practice, know that you are not doing anything wrong. See if you can offer compassion toward these difficult feelings, recognizing that they are a cue that you need warmth and kindness. If you are unable to return to a feeling of loving-kindness for yourself, take a break from this part of the practice. You might explore practicing loving-kindness for another and then return to practicing for yourself.

## Loving-Kindness for Another

Take a moment to bring to mind a person or being who has been a source of warmth, care, and connection for you. This might be a friend, mentor, teacher, pet, or spiritual figure. As you imagine this person or being in your mind's eye, notice how you feel in your body. You might visualize them sitting next to or in front of you. If you would like, begin to wish them well by quietly or silently repeating:

> May you be well.
> May you be kind to yourself.
> May you be safe from harm.
> May you be peaceful and at ease.

So long as the practice feels nourishing to you, repeat these phrases several more times, allowing the positive feeling of warmth to grow.

## Loving-Kindness for a Difficult Person

If you would like, I invite you to imagine someone who has been a source of difficulty for you. As you imagine this person or being, notice how you feel in your body. What emotions arise for you? If difficult feelings arise within you at this time, you might return to practicing loving-kindness for yourself to help you develop compassion for your pain. If you would like to continue, begin to visualize this person in your mind's eye. As you imagine them, you can choose how close or far away you would like them to be. You might then explore how it feels to offer loving-kindness to this person by quietly or silently repeating:

> May you be well.
> May you be kind to yourself.
> May you be safe from harm.
> May you be peaceful and at ease.

So long as the practice feels okay for you, repeat these phrases several more times. As you complete this process, allow the image of that person to fade away as you grow increasingly focused on the sights and sounds of your healing space. Take a moment to recognize that you engaged in a challenging yet skillful practice. Appreciate your courage. I encourage you to return to the loving-kindness meditation for yourself for a few breaths before completing this practice.

## Completion

What are you aware of now as you notice your body, mind, emotions, and level of energy? Take some time to write down any observations, knowing that you can return to this practice as often as you would like.

_____

_____

_____

_____

_____

_____

_____

_____

_____

_____

_____

_____

# The Subtle Body

All poses in yoga have energetic qualities. Some poses are invigorating and uplifting, while others are grounding and stabilizing. You can think of this as the direction that your prana, or life-force energy, flows within the pose. There are five directions in which your life-force energy can move, which are called the *vayus*, a Sanskrit word that means "winds."

The first of these is the *prana vayu* (not to be confused with prana itself), which is centered in the brain, heart, and lungs. This is an inward-moving energy that is associated with the inhalation. When this energy is balanced, you are likely to feel intellectually inspired, but when it is out of balance, you might be prone to worry or anxiety.

The second is the *apana vayu*, which is a downward-flowing energy associated with the exhalation and letting go. When it is out of balance, you might notice that you tend to hold on to your breath or emotions. This downward flow of energy is also associated with elimination, so a block here might show up as constipation. When this energy is flowing, you are more likely to feel grounded and relaxed.

The third pathway is *samana vayu*, which is a circulating energy associated with the core of your body at your navel. It is related to physical digestion, as well as processing or metabolizing your life experiences. When this energy is out of balance, you are more likely to feel overwhelmed or overextended. When samana vayu is flowing, you are more likely to feel creative and energetic.

The fourth pathway, *udana vayu*, is described as an upward-flowing energy that is located in the throat and supports communication. It also supports metabolism and is associated with the thyroid gland. When this energy is out of balance, you might feel blocked in your self-expression. In contrast, when flowing, udana vayu allows you to express yourself in an articulate and enthusiastic manner.

Finally, the fifth of these energetic pathways is *vyana vayu*, which is described as an expansive energy that extends throughout your entire body and is associated with the circulation of blood, lymph, and cerebral spinal fluid. While this expansion can feel exciting and playful, when it is out of balance, you might feel distracted, spacey, or unfocused.

These subtle energies are linked to key energy centers in the body called *chakras*, which is the Sanskrit word for "wheels." The chakras are located along the midline of the body at the pelvic floor, lower belly, diaphragm, chest, throat, forehead, and crown of your head. Each chakra has an endocrine system gland and concentration of nerves called a nerve plexus, which explains why we tend to feel a great deal of sensation in these areas of the body. Stress and trauma can lead you to feel blocked, carry excess tension, or feel disconnected in the areas of the body that correspond with these key energy centers. As a result, you might experience headaches, jaw tension, chronic sore throats, tension in your chest, digestive problems, or sexual dysfunction.

Paying attention to your internal body cues will help you explore the relationship between your chakras, physical tension, and your emotional health. For example, if you are feeling keyed up in fight or flight, you might notice bracing across your chest, tightness in your belly, or gripping in your pelvic floor. Or, if you are shut down in collapsed immobility, you might notice very little sensation or a feeling of collapse in these same areas. In order to cultivate awareness of the subtle cues of the energy in your body, it is beneficial to move slowly and mindfully. Moreover, because restorative postures provide a deep reset for your entire endocrine system, they are particularly beneficial for creating lasting energetic changes in body and mind.

As you deepen your yoga practice, you will increase awareness about how your energy is flowing. You can also become more fluent in directing your energy to best support you. For example, if you feel sluggish, you might need to focus on uplifting and expansive postures, whereas if you are feeling ungrounded or anxious, it can be helpful to focus on postures that help you feel rooted and relaxed.

Similarly, if you feel blocked—as if you are resisting the flow of energy and trying to push water uphill—you might want to explore allowing the energy to move through you like water following the path of least resistance. For example, you might move in a gentle, flowing manner, mimicking soft waves in the sea. Other times, you might notice that you feel a sort of stuck energy, which can manifest as specific body sensations, such as a knot of anxiety in your throat or belly. It is often said that your energy flows where your attention goes, so in these instances, you can create change simply by paying attention and breathing into your sensations. A balanced yoga practice helps you choose postures that enliven your body and mind through all of the vayus.

Since yoga works through the integration of polarities, each movement in yoga tends to have an equal and opposite movement of energy. For example, if you focus on downward movements by pressing into your legs, you will simultaneously feel an upward and expansive movement of energy. In yoga, we call this "root to rise," which essentially means that when you push into your feet, you will be better able to support your expansion without losing connection with yourself and the ground beneath you. The movement of subtle energy is just as important as the physical movements themselves. When you get to know these subtle energetic qualities, you can work to balance the flow of energy within each and every yoga pose. For example, when standing in mountain pose, you can simultaneously press downward with your feet, draw awareness into the core of your body, and lengthen your spine and arms upward, which will open across your chest and throat.

Advanced yogic practices work with the subtle movement of energy through a series of *bandhas* or "energy locks." Bandhas involve gentle contractions in three specific locations in the body. The first of these is the *mula bandha*, or the root lock, which is located at the pelvic floor. If you have experienced trauma, especially related to sexual abuse, contracting this part of your body might feel triggering or uncomfortable. On the other hand, some individuals find it empowering to engage in this practice, as it helps them feel that they are reclaiming or owning their body now.

The second energetic lock is the *uddiyana bandha*, which is described as an abdominal lift that creates a temporary contraction in the diaphragm. Uddiyana bandha is particularly beneficial for clearing stagnation from the digestive organs and lungs, but it needs to be practiced with care. The third energetic lock is *jalandhara bandha*, which is located at the throat chakra and is engaged by gently drawing your chin down and back. This lock can be thought of as the lid of the energetic container that helps you gather a potent felt sense of your presence. Since it is common for trauma to be held in the neck and throat, practicing this lock might evoke tender emotions of grief. While there is great value to practicing these energetic locks, they are best learned under the direction of a teacher who can tailor them to meet your individual needs or assist you to work through any associated somatic or emotional distress.

Even without directly practicing the advanced form of the bandhas, you can still indirectly integrate the concept of containing your energy. This is a valuable concept within your asana practice and is a way to bring the benefits of your yoga practice off the mat. Within your yoga practice, you might notice a surge of emotion. Now, you can pay attention to how you sense this emotion in your body. Perhaps you become aware of tension in your belly, chest, or throat. With awareness of sensation, you can then explore whether you will be served by releasing or discharging this emotion, or whether sustaining the charge of the feeling will be beneficial for your growth. If you choose to contain the emotion, you might imagine the glow of your inner light intensifying as you allow your breath, posture, and presence to be illuminated by this sensation. Maybe you grow a little taller, or perhaps you press firmly into your legs to sustain this charge. In doing so, you might notice that some new awareness or insight will arise.

You can also apply this concept of containing the charge of your energy throughout your day. For example, imagine that you are having a difficult conversation. You might begin to notice a charge in your body that evokes some discomfort. You might feel an urge to make yourself or the other person wrong. Discharging the emotion might lead you to collapse into sadness or storm off in anger. However, sustaining the emotional charge of discomfort might allow for a new possibility of self-expression or an increased ability to listen nondefensively, leading to a resolution of the conflict.

Exploring these energetic qualities within your yoga practice allows you to repeat the same posture day after day while recognizing that the nuances of your inner experience will vary. Tuning in to the subtle nature of the poses invites you to return with a beginner's mind to the simplest of practices with great curiosity about what new insight or awareness is possible for you. In doing so, you might discover that yoga offers an endless journey of self-study. This next practice is an invitation to explore these subtleties in tree pose, which will allow you to sense how sending your energetic roots into the ground helps you rise up with confidence.

# Root to Rise

This practice invites you to explore the subtle movement of energy in tree pose. A common misconception is that balance requires complete stillness; however, balance is actually achieved through a series of recalibrating movements that allow you to adjust the shape in subtle ways. For example, when you observe the actions of your standing foot and ankle in tree pose, you will notice micro-movements that help you to maintain the shape. This provides a lovely metaphor for the ways in which we respond to our changing needs by remaining flexible and adaptable. Imagine how trees withstand a windstorm: The ones that survive are able to move and bend like a willow, whereas the stiff and unyielding trees are more likely to fall.

Tree pose also offers a lovely metaphor for self-acceptance. When we look at trees in nature, we see that no two are exactly the same. The environment shapes each tree in a unique manner. We tend to appreciate the beauty of these asymmetries and imperfections in nature. You too have been shaped by the storms of your life. How might you appreciate your unique self-expression?

## Orienting and Centering

Find a comfortable place to stand for this practice. You can also adapt this posture by holding on to the top of a chair or touching the wall. Sometimes it is easier to balance while standing on a hard surface rather than on your yoga mat. It can also be easier to balance when your eyes are still rather than darting around, so you might find it helpful to choose one point on the floor in front of you for your gaze.

Beginning with two feet on the floor, I invite you to connect to your center with a few slow, mindful breaths. As you inhale, notice the sensations in your chest. As you exhale, send your awareness down through your belly, pelvis, legs, and feet. Continue breathing in this manner, and see if you can notice how your attention to your breath and body deepens your experience of this shape.

## Rooting

Now if you would like, choose which leg will be your standing leg. Imagine that this leg has roots that extend deep down into the earth. You might visualize that your standing leg is filled with sand, allowing it to feel heavy and weighted. Keep the knee of your standing leg slightly bent so you can actively press downward with your foot.

When you feel ready, begin to bring your opposite foot off the floor. Initially, you might simply lift your heel, keeping your toes on the ground. Or you might explore placing the sole of your lifted foot against the inside of your standing leg, either below or above your knee. Take your time to find your new sense of balance on one foot, and if you feel wobbly, return your attention to your standing leg as you imagine roots connecting deep into the earth. If your eyes have wandered, return your gaze to the point on the floor in front of you. Notice the small movements in your standing leg and ankle that help you maintain your balance in this shape.

## Rising

As you press down into your standing leg, begin to notice how the rest of your body responds. Explore allowing your spine to lengthen through the crown of your head. If you would like, you can expand on this upward-lifting energy as you bring your hands to your heart center. Press your palms together, and allow this to create a subtle opening through your chest and collarbones. If you would like, explore lifting your arms to become the branches of your tree.

Allow this shape to be unique to you, finding an expression that feels "just right" for today. Do you want your hands close to your body, or would you prefer to expand toward the sky? Would you like to flow and move as if the wind were rustling through the leaves, or would you prefer to be still within the shape? Notice how it feels to reach through your hands and fingertips. Allow yourself to expand.

If you fall out of balance, you can simply come back again. If you are unduly hard on yourself, see if you can invite a little gentleness. What might it be like to look at yourself in the same way you would view a tree in nature? How can this help you appreciate your resilient capacity to flexibly adapt to the challenges of your life?

### Receiving and Repeating

When you feel complete, slowly return your arms by your sides and place both of your feet onto the ground. Take your time between sides to notice the impact of this balancing posture. See if you can sense the subtle differences between the right and left sides of your body. When you feel ready, slowly repeat this process on the other side.

### Completion

What are you aware of now as you notice your body, mind, emotions, and level of energy? Take some time to write down any observations, knowing that you can return to this practice as often as you would like.

_____

_____

_____

_____

_____

_____

_____

_____

_____

_____

# Slow to Flow

As you grow increasingly comfortable with your yoga practice, the willful aspect of practice naturally gives way to an effortless quality in which you begin to surrender to the energetic flow of the poses. This kind of practice is called *vinyasa*, which means "to place in a special way." In particular, it reflects a fluid and rhythmic yoga practice in which you transition smoothly from one posture, or asana, into the next. In practice, the transitions between the shapes are just as important as the postures themselves. Moving in this manner, you allow your breath to initiate and illuminate each and every shape, with breath and movement being intricately connected. Without strain, you explore moving as if flowing through water, luxuriating in a smooth continuity of connected postures. The essence of vinyasa can be found in any moving sequence. For example, simply inhaling as you lift your arms up overhead and exhaling as you lower them to your sides allows you to explore this experience of flow.

One classic and well-known version of vinyasa is the sun salutation, which is a flowing sequence of shapes that moves from standing in mountain pose to forward fold, halfway lift, plank, cobra, downward facing dog, and back to mountain pose. A vinyasa practice comes full circle, allowing you to end where you began. The practice is like a *mala*, which is a beaded necklace used for meditation. Just like the mala, your moving meditation has a beginning, middle, and end.

Once you are comfortable with the basic form of a sun salutation, you can add other postures, such as chair pose, warrior poses, or triangle pose. The breath is the continuity that allows these shapes to feel like you are riding the waves in the sea. This can be a lovely flow, so long as it feels nourishing in your body. Importantly, you do not want to feel as if you are in choppy waters or a windstorm. Thus, attending to your breath is the key to an effortless vinyasa. If at any point you become short of breath or begin to hold your breath, this is a sign to return to stillness or engage in shorter movement sequences.

As your breath guides your movements—with each inhalation inviting an expansion and each exhalation allowing for a natural contraction—you begin to rhythmically expand and contract like a jellyfish undulating through the water. The Sanskrit word *spanda* refers to these pulsations that are found in all of nature. Spanda can be thought of as a vibration, movement, or wave that emanates out from and back to the center. Spanda is seen in the flower that opens at dawn and closes at the end of the day. These rhythmic oscillations are within you as well. Your heart, your lungs, and the tissues of the fascia all expand and contract. Your nervous system has expansive states—sometimes you feel energetic, playful, or joyful, while at other times you feel tired and draw inward. Just like the flower, you are not meant to remain closed. Spanda serves as a reminder that no single state defines you. You flow with the pulsations, expanding and contracting as you come back into alignment with your true nature.

Off your yoga mat, flow can be thought of as an effortless engagement with your environment in which your awareness and actions are synchronized (Csikszentmihalyi, 1990). Often, the experience of flow carries a feeling of rightness or of being fully awake. Flow can be found in any activity in which you carry a sense of mastery. For example, if you enjoy cooking, you may have felt this quality of immersion in the moment while moving through the kitchen, chopping vegetables, or spicing your favorite dish to perfection. You can witness this flow when watching well-trained athletes navigate the field or court—they move through space as if they can see what is about to happen and are already prepared. This experience of flow is something that is attainable for everyone, regardless of the challenges you have faced in your past or the circumstances of your present.

One of the beautiful aspects of developing a regular yoga practice is that it invites you to cultivate this sense of flow and mastery. As you return to the same set of postures again and again, you will develop increased familiarity and ease. The shapes begin to feel like old friends. Just like learning to play a piece of music on a piano, the first time is rarely smooth as you learn the notes and positioning for your fingers. However, with repeated practice, the patterns of the music become increasingly integrated into your muscle memory. Eventually, you no longer need to effortfully focus on reading the notes in order to create the beauty of music. The whole becomes greater than the sum of its parts as the music carries emotional depth and meaning.

I invite you to explore the next practice as a moving meditation. It integrates some of the shapes already introduced in previous chapters with new shapes to create a variation of vinyasa yoga. You can adapt this practice to meet your needs by doing only some of the practice or by modifying the shapes so they feel nourishing in your body. Remember the ethical principles of ahimsa (nonviolence) and satya (truthfulness), which serve as reminders to be gentle and honest with yourself. If you choose to explore the shapes, they might feel awkward or choppy the first time. However, as you return to and repeat this practice, they will grow increasingly familiar, and your movements will become smooth and fluid.

# Moving Meditation

This practice offers a slow progression through a sequence of postures with flowing arms that mimic waves on the ocean. As you grow increasingly comfortable with these shapes, you can revisit this sequence or add more shapes from other practices to create a flowing yoga practice that feels nourishing to your body and mind. The invitation is to explore these shapes in an effortless manner, linking movement to your breath in a moving meditation.

## Orienting and Centering

Find a comfortable place to stand for this practice. I invite you to begin by noticing your sensations, emotions, thoughts, and level of energy. This will serve as a baseline and will allow you to notice subtle changes in how you feel throughout the practice.

## Riding the Wave of Your Breath

To begin, I invite you to bring your attention to your breath. See if you can find a smooth, even rhythm to your breath, perhaps using a four-to-six-count cycle for your inhalation and exhalation. Notice how each breath rises, crests, and subsides like a gentle wave on the ocean. I encourage you to keep breathing in this rhythmic manner as you explore the postures. Notice if you lose connection to your breath or if it becomes choppy, and use this as a cue to slow down or rest in child's pose until you feel ready to proceed.

## Standing Side Bend Wave

From a standing position, I invite you to warm up your spine by taking a few side bends with your breath. As you inhale, draw both arms overhead, and as you exhale, bend to the right as your left arm curves overhead. At this same time, allow your right arm to curve in front of your body toward your left hip as you press your palms in opposite directions. Inhale as you lift back to center and then exhale as you bend to the left and move your arms in the opposite direction. As you move from side to side, allow your arms to move like waves on the sea. Continue moving with your breath as you inhale to center and exhale to each side for two or three more repetitions. To complete, inhale as you return to center, and draw both arms back overhead for mountain pose.

### Mountain Pose Flow

I invite you to explore the relationship between your feet and the ground beneath you in a mountain pose. Focus on your connection to the earth, and as you inhale, begin to bring your arms up along the sides of your body until they are overhead. On an exhalation, lower your arms until they rest by your sides. Repeat this movement of your arms as you inhale and exhale two or three more times.

### Forward Fold and Halfway Lift

Continuing to move with your breath, inhale your arms up overhead and exhale as you fold forward over your legs. See if you can keep your knees slightly bent to reduce tension in your lower back and legs. Slowly inhale as you explore coming to a halfway lift and lengthen your spine by placing your fingertips on the floor, on your shins, or on blocks in front of you. Then exhale as you return to the forward fold. Inhale again and return to standing in mountain pose as you lift your arms overhead. Exhale as you lower your hands by your sides.

If you would like, repeat this forward-fold sequence as you mindfully stay connected to your body and breath.

### Plank Pose to the Earth

Continuing to move with your breath, from a forward fold, inhale to a halfway lift, and exhale as you step your feet back to a high plank position. Since this shape often requires both upper body and core strength, it may feel somewhat effortful. However, can you infuse the shape with joy? As needed, you can modify this shape by placing your knees down onto your yoga mat. In either variation, keep your core strong as you slowly exhale and drop your body all the way down to your mat, while keeping your elbows hugging toward your sides.

## Cobra

Once you arrive on your mat, your next inhalation will lift your upper body into cobra pose. To find this shape, place your hands on the mat under your shoulders while continuing to hug your elbows toward your sides. With the tops of your feet and legs pressing firmly into the earth, inhale as you press into your hands to lift your chest off the floor. You get to choose how much weight you place into your hands and how much height you explore as you lift through your shoulders and chest. On an exhalation, lower back down onto the mat. Once again, you can repeat this shape by moving with your breath, lifting as you inhale and lowering as you exhale.

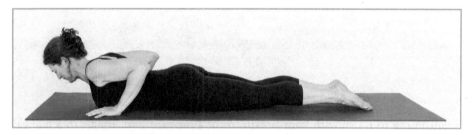

## Downward Facing Dog

To transition from cobra into downward facing dog, inhale as you move your body into tabletop or high plank, and as you exhale, send your hips high as you lengthen through your legs. Pause here with several breaths as you press into your hands and feet and send your breath and awareness throughout your entire body. When you feel complete, walk your feet forward to the front of your mat until you return to a forward fold. Once again, find a halfway lift and lower. Then return to mountain pose. This is the completion of one full sun salutation. You can repeat the sequence as many times as you would like.

### Warrior Two Wave

If you feel ready to continue onward from downward facing dog, I invite you to exhale as you step your right foot forward between your hands, moving into a lunge shape. Do not worry if you need to take a few steps to arrive in this low lunge; you will build the strength to step forward with repeated practice. From a low lunge, your right toes will face the short side of your yoga mat, in line with your knee, while your left toes will angle slightly forward. This practice offers a variation of warrior two by inviting you to flow with your breath as you move your torso and arms in the same manner as you did with the side bend variation earlier in this sequence.

This time, inhale as you reach away from your right leg, curving your right hand overhead as your curl your left arm underneath. On the exhalation, lean slightly forward as your left arm curves overhead and your right arm curls underneath. Continue to move with this variation of warrior two, allowing your breath to guide the movement of your arms like waves on the ocean.

After several breaths in this manner or when you feel complete, exhale as you bring your hands all the way to the earth. Step your right foot back into downward facing dog. If you would like, pause here with several breaths as you press into your hands and feet and send your breath and awareness throughout your entire body. Check in with your breath, knowing that you can rest in child's pose at any time. When you feel ready, I invite you to step your left foot forward into a low lunge and explore this moving meditation on the opposite side. When complete, you will arrive in downward facing dog and then lower your knees to rest in child's pose.

## Completion

Remain in child's pose for as long as you would like. When you feel ready, slowly return to a seated position. What are you aware of now as you notice your body, mind, emotions, and level of energy? Take some time to write down any observations, knowing that you can return to this practice as often as you would like.

_____

_____

_____

_____

_____

_____

_____

_____

_____

_____

_____

_____

_____

_____

_____

# The Gift of Humility

Strength comes in many forms. It can come in the form of being assertive and empowered to stand up for your rights, as well as in the complementary power that comes with vulnerability and humility. Although many of us alternate between feeling desirable and special and feeling unworthy and undeserving, humility allows us to recognize that we are neither inferior nor superior to other people. The gift of humility allows us to relate to ourselves and others with acceptance for things just as they are. With humility, we are not trying to rise above the world.

Humility also helps us recognize that there are common experiences that unite us all as humans. We all have experienced the first separation that comes with being born. We each eventually must leave our childhood homes and let go of dependence on our parents or caregivers. We are all faced with the profound task of taking responsibility for our own lives. At some point, each of us will lose someone we love to death, and we all must face the inevitable reality that we, too, will die. Cultivating this humility is an act of maturation; it is a stage of our development that is often accompanied by invisible yet palpable growing pains.

In addition, humility asks us to contemplate how we use our power and privilege. Humility requires that we let go of the need to be right and acknowledge that we do not have all of the answers. There are so many things out of balance in our world, including prejudicial treatment of people who fall outside of the dominant group, unequal pay based on gender and race, inequitable access to basic health care, hunger and food insecurity, and an imbalanced relationship between humans and the earth. When our life decisions and behaviors are rooted in humility, we are better able to take personal responsibility for our impact in the world so that we can actively take part in redistributing power, wealth, and access to resources for all people.

An imbalanced use of power can also show up internally in how we speak to or treat ourselves. We all have parts of ourselves that we prefer to relate to and parts that we would rather avoid. Often, this can lead to marginalization of the parts of ourselves that carry the pain of unresolved wounds. For example, perhaps as a child, you received the message that you were "too much" or "not enough." This is a wound that you continue to carry inside you by pushing away the parts of yourself that are hurting the most. By healing these internal wounds, you can be kinder toward yourself and reduce your reliance on defensive, self-protective patterns that prevent you from being vulnerable and sensitive to other people's suffering. Thus, this personal work becomes the foundation for world work.

Healing from trauma ultimately asks you to take personal responsibility for your wounds. This is true whether you are healing from a single traumatic event, ongoing abuse, or the subtle accumulation of emotional neglect. Taking personal responsibility doesn't mean that you do not need support. Rather, taking responsibility involves having the humility to recognize when you need to seek out the support of another person.

By attending to your own suffering, you are more likely to carry respect and sensitivity for the suffering of others. You recognize that no one is invulnerable to the challenges of being human, especially when you recognize that there is an extensive history of collective trauma that has been carried across generations. This journey of personal responsibility is an invitation to engage in saucha, which involves taking personal responsibly for your thoughts and behaviors so you are living in greater alignment with your soul's purpose.

You can practice humility on the yoga mat each time you engage in beginner's mind, which acknowledges that you can always learn something new. In this way, you practice bowing to the unknown as a symbolic reminder of how you might approach your own healing journey. Bowing to the unknown invites you to live in the unplanned moment without an agenda. Here, you can surrender the need to be right, to know the answers, and you can humbly trust that which you cannot see. This process is a leap of faith—one that requires the willingness to temporarily suspend what you know in order to be with the unknown.

The following practice invites you to explore moving between warrior one and humble warrior poses as a means of cultivating your own vulnerability and humility. The act of bowing forward lowers your head beneath your physical heart, an action that invites you to surrender your thinking mind as you dive into the wisdom of your spiritual heart.

# Bowing to the Unknown

This practice invites you to slowly and mindfully explore two yoga postures: warrior one and humble warrior. While both of these postures can be physically challenging, the invitation is to engage in the subtle and symbolic nature of these shapes. To support your practice, you may also find it helpful to have two blocks and a strap for the second pose.

## Orienting and Centering

I invite you to begin by standing in mountain pose as you notice your sensations, emotions, thoughts, breath, and level of energy.

## Warrior One

When you feel ready, move into a lunge position by stepping your right foot forward so it is facing the front of your mat. Bend your right knee and keep your left leg straight behind you, positioning your left toes so they angle toward the front left corner of your mat. In this shape, your hips will also begin to shift toward the front of your mat, but there is no need to force this process, so stop whenever your hips find their natural point of resistance. From here, you can explore bringing your torso toward the front of your mat.

On an inhalation, explore lifting your arms up overhead. Once again, if you feel resistance in your shoulders, this is an important place to stop as you honor your body. As with the previous postures, notice how it feels to press downward in your feet, which will facilitate a lifting action in your torso and arms. Bring attention to your breath and explore any adjustments to the shape that allow you to arrive more fully in this pose. I invite you to take about three to five deep breaths to deepen your experience. Prior to moving into the opposite side, I invite you to continue directly into the next humble warrior pose.

## Humble Warrior

When you feel complete with the first posture of warrior one, exhale as you lower your arms to interlace your hands behind your lower back. If you would like to clasp your hands but cannot reach, you can use a strap to create more ease in the shape. Remember to be honest with yourself and that there is no need to push yourself in these postures. Inhale as you gently lift your heart up toward the sky. You might stay here for a few breaths, and when you feel ready, begin to fold forward to the inside of your right knee. As you do so, you have an invitation to bring your clasped hands up behind you as you lower your head below your heart. If you prefer, you can lower your hands to blocks, as this will provide you with more support in this shape.

In whichever version of this posture you have found, take about three to five deep breaths to deepen your experience. When you feel complete, slowly lift back up and step forward into mountain pose prior to exploring warrior one and humble warrior on the opposite side.

## Completion

When you feel complete, pause into mountain pose. If you would like, complete this active practice by resting in stillness while seated or lying on your back. When you are ready, notice what you are aware of now in your body, mind, emotions, and level of energy. Take some time to write down any observations, knowing that you can return to this practice as often as you would like.

_____

_____

_____

_____

_____

_____

_____

_____

_____

_____

_____

# Opening to Love

As your yoga practice evolves over time, the journey might feel like a process of peeling back layers. As if slowly peeling an onion, deeper aspects of yourself are revealed as you work your way through the healing process. Perhaps, instead of an onion, you might imagine peeling off the leaves of an artichoke as a reminder that you are releasing the layers that defend and protect your heart. You are revealing and unmasking your authentic self. This process of opening to love can feel vulnerable, as so many of us have been hurt or betrayed. At some point, it may have felt necessary to close down around your heart. However, staying closed often leads to feelings of resignation and loneliness. Grieving these losses and hurts is often an inevitable part of this journey of opening the heart.

Because your heart carries your deepest desire to belong and your most vulnerable wounds of rejection, touching into these tender places can evoke shame or a belief that there is something fundamentally wrong with you. This is especially true if these wounds began in childhood. Early experiences of abandonment, rejection, parental disinterest, and abuse are profoundly confusing for a child. Developmentally, young children are sensitive, and when a parent treats them poorly, the wound goes straight to the heart. A child may even come to believe that the parent's pain is their fault.

If your open heart was once met with criticism as a child, the wound of not being "good enough" can become a deep-seated sense of self that carries into adulthood. Around this core wound of rejection, you may have built up a wall to protect against future pain. This might manifest as the avoidance of intimacy, or you might carry so much resentment and anger that you hurt others. Physically, you might hunch your shoulders and close off around your chest, or alternatively, you might walk through the world braced as if wearing an impenetrable shell.

It takes courage to lay down your armor—you are taking the risk of being hurt again. Choosing to engage wholeheartedly in this complex and hurting world is a profound spiritual path. To lead with an open heart, you must learn to turn toward your own wounds while simultaneously recognizing that the events of your past do not need to define your future. You must also learn to relate to the pain that others carry without becoming overwhelmed. This requires recognizing that you are not responsible for their pain. You do not need to protect others from their difficult feelings or yours. You develop the capacity to connect to others without losing a connection to yourself.

However, even the most carefully chosen and well-intentioned loved ones will sometimes hurt your feelings. You, too, will sometimes hurt theirs. Yet you can remain open-hearted as you navigate these conflicts. This, too, is yoga. It is the wisdom that comes with being able to sit with polarities and contradictions as they exist in and around you. Your breath becomes an ally to help you navigate the stormy seas of life. You develop a greater capacity to compassionately relate to pain while preserving hope that this can provide fertile ground for growth.

In addition, opening to love is an invitation to move beyond the reactive states of fight or flight, allowing you to discover that you are here not simply to survive, but to become the creator of your life. To open your heart involves being open to both giving and receiving love. You might notice that you feel comfortable giving to others or taking care of them, but receiving care might feel too vulnerable. However, giving and receiving are deeply intertwined actions. Allowing yourself to receive love from another person allows them to give to you. As you feel nourished by the loving presence of others, you will be better supported to share your love without feeling depleted or drained.

The physical practice of yoga offers a very tangible way to practice this process of opening to love without giving yourself away. For example, heart-opening postures can help you release tension from your shoulders, chest, neck, throat, and upper back. They also emphasize the expansive and uplifting movement of the prana vayu (inward-flowing energy), udana vayu (upward-flowing energy), and vyana vayu (expansive energy). Since yoga always emphasizes the union of opposites, it is equally valuable to stay rooted in apana vayu (downward-flowing energy) and samana vayu (circulating energy) so that you simultaneously remain tethered to your core and your sense of self. This helps ensure that you do not give too much of yourself away—you stay anchored in self-love as you open your heart to the world.

The following practice offers three heart-opening postures. The first is a seated variation of yogic seal pose, which involves bowing your head to the wisdom of your heart while clasping your hands behind you to open up through the back of your heart. This is followed by camel pose, which is an active pose that focuses on grounding through your legs, tethering to your core, and simultaneously opening across your chest and throat. This active pose is complemented by a restorative heart-opening posture in supported fish pose.

Patience is a key to self-discovery. Just as you cannot force a flower to open, this practice invites a gentle unfolding into this truth. It is about showing up fully for yourself and softening the defenses that were once necessary. While you cannot predict whether or when you will face future loss or rejection, you can temporarily explore how it feels to open to love. As you let go of your defenses, you also have an opportunity to awaken to new possibilities. It is your birthright to experience this love.

# Heart Opening

I invite you to explore this short sequence of heart-opening postures. As you open your heart in these poses, allow your breath to move through you like a gentle breeze. It is helpful to have two blocks and a bolster for the final shape in this sequence. You might also benefit from having a strap or a blanket.

## Orienting and Centering

I invite you to begin seated on your yoga mat. If possible, explore sitting on your heels with your knees bent. If this seated position is not available to you, you might choose to sit on a block or with a blanket between your hips and your heels. Take a moment to notice your sensations, emotions, thoughts, breath, and level of energy.

## Yogic Seal Pose

To prepare for this shape, remain seated on your heels, and bring your arms behind you to interlace your hands behind your lower back. If you would like to clasp your hands but cannot reach, you can use a strap to create more ease in the shape. Remember to be honest with yourself and that there is no need to push yourself in these postures. Once you have found your version of this shape, I invite you to inhale as you draw your clasped hands down behind you and gently lift your heart up toward the sky. Perhaps you lift your chin slightly, feeling the movement of your breath through your throat.

You might stay here for a few breaths, then if you would like, begin to fold forward, allowing your head to lower to the earth or onto a bolster for support. At the same time, lift your clasped hands up behind you. Perhaps explore how it feels to gently squeeze your shoulder blades together behind you as you take several deep breaths. Notice how you can simultaneously open the front of your shoulders and chest as you create this gentle contraction in your upper back. After several breaths, slowly lift up and release your hands by your sides. Take some time to receive the subtle movement of energy that is released from this shape.

## Camel Pose

If you are practicing on your yoga mat, lift your legs off your heels, allowing your shins to remain pressed into the floor, and come into a kneeling shape. I will offer two variations of camel, both of which are beneficial for opening the heart. The first, gentler variation is to bring your hands behind your lower back for support with your fingers pointed up or down. Your hands will help you press your pelvis slightly forward. Press downward through your shins as you begin to lift and arch your torso upward. You can keep your chin tucked or slightly lifted depending on what feels comfortable in your neck. It is wise not to drop your head back, as this can create injury or excess tension. You do not want to experience any pain in your neck or lower back. Explore your edge in this shape.

If you feel comfortable here, you might explore a second variation of this pose by bringing your hands down to your heels or ankles while keeping your torso arched upward. It can be helpful to tuck your toes under, which will lift your heels and make this shape more accessible. Remember, none of these shapes are better or worse; you are simply discovering the edge of sensation that serves you today.

Take as long as you would like in your chosen variation of this shape, and when you feel complete, slowly lower your hips until you are once again sitting on your heels or in any comfortable seated position for your body. Take some time to receive the subtle movement of energy that is released from this shape.

## Supported Fish Pose

The final pose in this sequence invites you to explore a restorative heart opener using blocks and a bolster to support you in fish pose. Begin by placing one medium-height block lengthwise on your mat where your shoulder blades will rest, and a second block of medium or taller height to go under your head. Place a bolster over the blocks to create a soft landing, and then slowly lower yourself onto this support. It can take a bit of adjusting until you find the right position.

Once you find a shape that feels supportive for you, allow your legs to extend out long in front of you, and open your arms to your sides with your palms facing up. If you notice discomfort in your lower back, bend your knees and place the soles of your feet on the floor. You can adjust the position of your arms until the posture feels supportive to you. See if you can allow your shoulders to soften while relaxing your face, jaw, and throat. So long as you are comfortable, you are welcome to stay in this shape for as long as you would like.

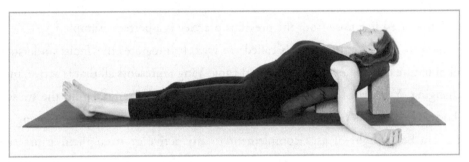

## Completion

When you feel complete, slowly bend your knees and roll off your bolster and blocks until you are resting comfortably on your side. Rest here for several breaths, and when you feel ready, press back up into a comfortable sitting position. What are you aware of now in your body, mind, emotions, and level of energy? Take some time to write down any observations, knowing that you can return to this practice as often as you would like.

_____

_____

_____

_____

_____

_____

_____

_____

# The Soft Side of Yoga

As we wind down this experiential journey through yoga, the final sections of this chapter focus on the softer side of yoga by inviting you into restorative postures that support your parasympathetic nervous system. Restorative yoga focuses on longer holds in restful poses. You might hold a pose for five minutes while allowing yourself to soften into the stillness of the shape. Often, these poses are supported through the use of bolsters, blankets, and blocks. (Supported fish pose from the previous practice is a perfect example.)

One form of restorative yoga is called *yin yoga*. It integrates the Taoist understanding that all of nature carries polarities of yin and yang. Yang represents all that is active, moving, and changing. Yang yoga practices emphasize moving and strengthening the muscles of your body. On the other hand, yin represents that which is stable and unmoving. A yin practice can be thought of as a complement to any active or strengthening practice—it is the soft side of yoga. Yin postures focus on your ligaments, tendons, and connective tissue. Since the capacity to stretch the tendons and ligaments is limited compared to the muscles, the joints benefit from longer holds in stillness, which creates healthy stress in these tissues of your body. This is facilitated by engaging in shapes that intelligently, and safely, compress the joints of your hips and lower back by using the weight of your own body in hip-opening, twisting, and forward-folding positions.

Yin yoga also stimulates the meridians of the body. Meridians can be thought of as channels of energy that are connected to the major organs of the body, such as the heart, lungs, kidneys, liver, and stomach. These meridian lines parallel how fascial lines are connected throughout the body, as they run through the center of the body out through the legs, arms, and face (Dorsher, 2009; Myers & Hillman, 2004). The restorative postures of yin yoga open up these channels to facilitate the movement of subtle energy or vayus, which will enhance your felt sense of self as integrated and whole. The longer holds in yin yoga postures can help to release physical tension and the weight of heavy emotions as you breathe in the shape.

In addition, when you combine restorative practices with a contemplative mindset, you can downregulate into states of calmness (Porges, 2017). However, a sense of safety is always rooted in choice, and resting in stillness can never be forced. Just as you may need to build up tolerance to engage in strength training or endurance exercises, you may also need to build up a tolerance for restful states. As you work to build this tolerance, you might find that when your body becomes still, your mind speeds up. You might feel restless or notice the urge to fidget. Or you might feel collapsed or immobilized. Remember that you can move your body freely as needed and that you can turn toward cues that help you recognize that you are safe now. Once you recognize that you are safe, you can practice learning to let go of your vigilance and soften into stillness.

Each restorative shape offers you an opportunity to invoke an inward turn, direct your attention away from the stimulation of the outer world, and nourish yourself with your own awareness. As with all of the practices in this book, yin yoga invites you to find your edge in each pose. This might be the first sign of resistance or discomfort. Then you pause, observe, and breathe into your experience just as it is. Since yin practices involve longer holds, you will have an opportunity to notice what happens when you marinate in a shape for several minutes. Often, you will notice a release that allows you to deepen into the shape until your find the next edge, which offers another opportunity to pause, observe, and breathe as you deepen your journey of self-acceptance.

The next practice provides you with an opportunity to explore a restorative yin yoga sequence for yourself. The postures are focused on releasing tension through your hips and lower back. Remember, if you experience physical pain at any time, you have gone too far, and if uncomfortable emotions arise, you can gauge how long to stay in the experience while always recognizing that you can come out of a pose at any time.

# Turning Inward

This gentle, restorative yin yoga sequence invites you to explore longer holds in postures aimed to release tension in your hips and lower back. The forward folds in this practice involve rounding your spine over your legs, but if you have a history of joint hypermobility, sciatica, or back injuries, these poses may be contraindicated for you. If you do choose to come into these shapes, it will be helpful to have two blocks, a bolster, and a blanket for this practice. While it is recommended that you stay in some of the poses for three to five minutes, you can come out of any pose at any time. If you would like, you might also choose to play some soft music that evokes a calm or loving feeling for you.

## Orienting and Centering

I invite you to begin seated comfortably on your yoga mat. Take a moment to notice your sensations, emotions, thoughts, breath, and level of energy.

## Butterfly

For this shape, bring the soles of your feet together and slide them away from you. If it is safe for your lower back, allow your spine to round as you fold forward. You might allow your hands to rest on your feet or on the floor in front of you. Or you can explore resting your head into your hands with your elbows resting on blocks. It can also be helpful to lift your hips up slightly by

sitting on a folded blanket. Stay in the shape for about three to five minutes, and when you are ready to come out of the shape, slowly use your hands to press yourself up out of the forward fold. You can then lean back on your hands and slowly straighten your legs. If you notice any stiffness, you might rock your legs from side to side to release your hips.

## Half Butterfly

From a seated position, bend your right leg and straighten your left leg as you draw your right foot to the inside of your left leg. To facilitate this pose, you might find it helpful to lift your hips up slightly by sitting on a folded blanket. In the first version of this shape, explore folding forward over your left leg. If it is safe for your lower back, allow your back to round as you fold toward your leg. If needed, you can bend your left leg by placing a bolster or blanket under your knee for support. You can also place your hands on the floor for support, use blocks under your elbows, or use a bolster on top of your leg to support your torso.

After about two minutes, you can come into a second variation of this shape by adding a twist to your spine. To create this change, lift your torso up slightly and draw your right arm to the inside of your left leg on the floor or on a block. This will allow you to lean the right side of your body down toward your left leg. Your right hand might rest on top of your left hip, or you might extend your right arm overhead as you gently rotate your torso up toward the sky. Once again, breathe into this shape for about two minutes. When you feel ready to come out of the pose, turn your torso back down toward the floor and use both hands to slowly press yourself up to sitting. Take a few moments to stretch out through both legs before moving to the other side.

### Shoelace

This classic hip opener can be beneficial for the joints of your lower body, but you can skip this shape if it creates pain in your knees. Once again, it can be helpful to lift your hips up slightly by sitting on a folded blanket. Begin in a seated position, with your legs extended out in front of you, and draw your right leg over your left leg, sliding your right heel toward your left hip as far as it will go. Then bend your left knee and draw your left foot toward your right thigh, gently sliding it as far as it will go. In this position, your knees will be stacked on top of each other. If your bottom knee has discomfort, you can modify this shape by extending your left leg long in front of you.

Now gently begin to fold forward while rounding your spine. Once again, you can support your head in your hands by placing your elbows on your knees. See how it feels to stay in the shape for about three to five minutes, and when you are ready to come out of the shape, slowly use your hands to press yourself up out of the forward fold. You can then lean back on your hands and slowly straighten your legs. If you notice any stiffness, you might rock your legs from side to side to release your hips before coming into the shape on the opposite side.

### Deer

This next pose helps open and balance your hips after shoelace pose, but you can skip it if it creates pain in your knees. Starting in butterfly pose, slowly swing your right leg behind you so the side of your right foot is resting on the floor. You can then move your left foot slightly away from your body so your front leg is at a right angle. If you have enough sensation in your right hip in this shape, allow yourself to remain here as you connect to your breath. If you need to move deeper into the shape in order to find your edge, you can begin to twist toward the left, which will amplify sensations in your right hip. To do so, walk your left hand behind you as you twist to the left. You might rest your right hand on your left leg. Explore this shape for about one minute, and when you are ready to come out of the shape, slowly bring your torso and legs to center and come into the shape on the opposite side.

## Happy Baby

For this next hip opener, come down onto your back. Once you are lying on your back, hug your knees to your chest and use your hands to grip the outside of your calves, ankles, or soles of your feet as you send your feet up toward the sky. Continue to release your shoulders and head down to the floor. Unlike the previous shapes, you might find some exploratory movements in this shape by sending your feet out to each side one by one. Allow yourself to find a playful exploration in this pose. When you feel complete, slowly draw your legs back to center and rest your feet onto the mat.

## Wind-Removing Pose and Reclining Twist

Now, if you would like, bring both knees up toward your chest once again. You might wrap your arms around your shins as if giving yourself a hug. Pause here and perhaps rock a little from side to side to massage your digestive organs. Now, keeping hold of your right knee, extend your left leg long in front of you. Once again, you can wrap your hands or forearms around your right shin. Take several breaths here, either in stillness or as you try adding a few gentle pulses into your right leg with your hands.

From here, I invite you to draw your right knee across your body toward the left. Ideally, your right shoulder will remain on the floor, but if it is floating, you can place a folded blanket underneath your shoulder for support. There is no need to push your right knee toward the floor; rather, you might place a block under your knee for support. Explore this shape for about three to five minutes. When you are ready to come out of the shape, slowly lift your knees to center and extend both legs out long prior to finding this shape on the opposite side.

## Legs up the Wall

The final posture in this practice can be completed by moving to a wall, which will allow you to rest your legs on it for support. I invite you to lie down on the floor near a wall, moving your bottom as close to the wall as possible, as you gently scoot your legs up on the wall until your body resembles an L shape. You might place a folded blanket or bolster underneath your hips and then lift your legs so that you can rest your heels on the wall. Take time to find your way into this shape. Adjust your position until you feel supported. Alternatively, you can use a chair for this pose, allowing your calves to rest on the seat of the chair so your legs are at a ninety-degree angle instead of extending straight up.

Once you have found a comfortable position, begin to draw your awareness inside. See if you can feel the heaviness of your body, and explore how it feels to soften into support. If it feels right for you, you might choose to rest in this shape for closer to ten minutes, knowing that you have the option to move out of this shape at any time. When you feel ready, slowly descend your legs, and roll onto one side.

## Completion

Take as much time as you need resting on your side. When you feel ready, press back up into a comfortable sitting position. What are you aware of now as you notice your body, mind, emotions, and level of energy? Take some time to write down any observations, knowing that you can return to this practice as often as you would like.

_____

_____

_____

_____

_____

_____

_____

# Settling into Stillness

The most profound integration of your yoga practice happens when you allow yourself to rest. Resting into stillness gives you time to absorb the new patterns that you created in your practice. Integrating these changes into your overall sense of self is what allows you to transform over time. Settling into stillness also allows you to access the inner wisdom that can be found within the depths of your psyche. As if diving deep below the surface of the ocean, you find the slowest-moving currents of your soul's wisdom. Within these depths, you connect to your intuition. As you reside in this deep connection to your heart, you learn to trust this inner knowing, which becomes the guiding compass for your life's decisions.

In order to rest into this place of deep stillness, you must feel safe enough to let go of your defenses, which will allow you to access your parasympathetic nervous system's relaxation response (Benson & Proctor, 2011; Wang et al., 2010). With this felt sense of safety, you can access a hybrid vagal state that engages both the ventral vagal complex (social engagement system) and the dorsal vagal complex. This blended nervous system state facilitates your rest-and-digest response. However, reclaiming a healthy relationship to stillness can take time to develop and requires patience. Therefore, if at any point in the practice you sense that you are feeling unsafe, you can climb the polyvagal ladder by adding in some movement so you don't feel stuck in an immobilization response (Dana, 2018).

Rest is such an important part of any yoga practice because our bodies are ruled by rhythm. The rhythmic pulse of your heartbeat and the cyclical nature of your circadian rhythm are two clear examples. Your circadian rhythm is a twenty-four-hour cycle that is not only responsible for your sleep patterns but also helps regulate your hormones, body temperature, hunger cycles, and digestion. When your circadian rhythm gets offset by a significant disruption to your schedule (such as jet lag), it can impact both your sleep and your digestion. Our bodies appreciate when we go to sleep, wake up, and eat with relative predictability. When we engage in restorative practices and meditation with regularity, our bodies become accustomed to these rhythms as well.

Although rest is an integral part of our body's rhythm, many of us have a complicated relationship to rest. That's because our culture conditions us to believe that our self-worth is based on productivity. You might feel guilty for resting or believe that it is selfish to take time off. You might fear that if you slow down, you will miss an opportunity. Maybe you fear that you will lose momentum or that you will become stagnant. Perhaps you have received messages that you're lazy if you're not working hard or being productive. These ingrained messages can cause you to neglect your health or believe that "hard work" is what brings happiness.

Sadly, this can lead you to feel disconnected from your deeper self, and you might question the point of all this hard work. Over time, an addiction to busyness can also lead to burnout, which can affect your endocrine system functioning and overall physical health (Bayes et al., 2021). Cultivating a nourishing relationship to rest takes consistency and practice. Paradoxically, when you do embrace the need for rest, you tend to be more focused and attentive during the day, which can ultimately allow you to be more productive.

Classically, *shavasana*, or corpse pose, is the final posture of any asana practice. This resting shape invites you to lie down comfortably on your back while noticing your breath and body as you descend into the quiet space of no actions and no productivity. This involves sensing the heaviness in your body. You have an opportunity to focus on being present, receiving the gifts from your practice, and to soften into the support of the earth beneath you. While this might look like a nap, it is actually an opportunity to remain fully conscious yet relaxed. Rather than trying to change yourself, you practice welcoming yourself, just as you are. While you might ultimately build up your capacity to rest in this pose for ten or fifteen minutes, you might need to start with shorter practice times.

*Yoga nidra*, or yogic sleep, is another type of restorative practice that is particularly beneficial for nervous system health (Moszeik et al., 2020). Yoga nidra involves resting in corpse pose while engaging in a series of guided body-awareness scans. Traditionally, this practice begins by setting an intention, which helps you connect to a deep sense of meaning or purpose to your practice. Yoga nidra typically lasts between thirty and forty minutes, but if you are prone to hypoarousal, it can be beneficial to begin with a shorter, ten-minute practice of stillness while you focus your awareness on your breath and bodily sensations. As needed, you can also adapt your yoga nidra practice to reduce the likelihood of triggering PTSD symptoms by choosing to sit up or keep your eyes open. You can choose to move your body or end the practice at any time. If you would like to try this for yourself, the following practice offers you an opportunity to explore a trauma-sensitive version of yoga nidra with these adaptations in mind.

# A Restorative Reset

As you explore this yoga nidra practice, you are welcome to adapt it in any way that best supports you. You can vary the length of the time that you engage in the practice, remain seated instead of lying down, or choose to keep your eyes open the entire time. I recommend recording the practice for yourself or having someone you trust record it for you so you can experience the gift of effortlessly being guided through yoga nidra.

## Orienting and Centering

I invite you to begin by choosing whether you would like to lie down on your mat or find a comfortable and supported seated position. If you are lying down, you might choose to place a bolster under your knees, rest your head on a pillow, or cover yourself with a blanket for warmth. As you settle in, take a moment to notice your sensations, emotions, thoughts, breath, and level of energy. If you would like, perhaps set aside any thoughts or items from your to-do list so you can be fully present for this restorative reset for your body and mind.

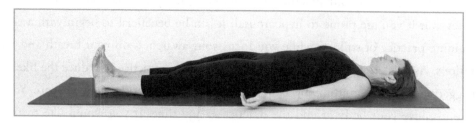

## Intention Setting

Now take a moment to reflect on a time when you felt connected to yourself in a positive and loving manner. Where were you? Who helped you developed this deep sense of connection to yourself? How do you feel in your body as you recall this time, place, or supportive person? As you sense this feeling in your body, is there a word or short phrase that matches this feeling? Here are some examples: content, peaceful, expansive, open, safe, flowing, connected, at ease, comfortable, secure, balanced, relaxed.

Once you have found a word that matches this deep feeling of connection and support, you can create a short phrase by adding "I am" to your chosen word. For example, if your word is *balanced*, you would simply say to yourself, "I am balanced." Once you have arrived at your chosen intention for today, I invite you to repeat your intention several times to yourself as you sense the associated feeling in your body. You can also repeat your intention at any time throughout this practice to help you return to a peaceful felt sense of connection, ease, and support.

## Guided Awareness of Your Face and Neck

At this point, I will guide you to bring your attention to your body, one area at a time. To begin, I invite you to bring your attention to your face by noticing the sensations in your jaw, mouth, ears, nose, cheeks, eyes, forehead, and scalp. Draw your attention to the back of your neck, your chin, the front of your neck, and the inner sensations of your throat. While you might choose to remain still, you are also welcome to create small movements in your face and jaw or soft sounds to increase your sensory awareness of your face and neck. If you would like, create a gentle squeeze to contract the muscles in your face and neck and then let the tension go. Repeat this if you would like, and then take two or three additional breaths while noticing the sensations in your face and neck.

## Guided Awareness of Your Arms

Now I invite you to bring your attention to your left shoulder, left arm, left palm, and left fingers. Then shift your awareness to your right shoulder, right arm, right palm, and right fingers. While you might choose to remain still, you are also welcome to create small movements by gently tensing and releasing the muscles in your shoulders and arms, opening and closing your hands, or wiggling your fingers if this helps you sense and feel your arms and hands. Then take a few breaths as you notice the sensations in your shoulders, arms, and hands.

## Guided Awareness of Your Torso

Now I invite you to bring your attention to the sensations in your torso. Become aware of your front and back side as you notice the sensations in your upper back, lower back, chest, and belly. Notice your pelvis and sacrum. While you might choose to remain still, you are also welcome to take a deep breath in as you lift and stretch your belly and chest, and then release this stretch as you exhale. Then take two or three breaths while noticing the sensations in your entire torso.

## Guided Awareness of Your Legs

Now I invite you to bring your attention to your left hip, left leg, left foot, and left toes. Then shift your awareness to your right hip, right leg, right foot, and right toes. While you might choose to remain still, you are also welcome to create small movements by gently tensing and relaxing the muscles of your legs or by wiggling your toes if this helps you sense and feel your legs and feet. Then take two or three breaths while noticing the sensations in your hips, legs, and feet.

## Guided Awareness of Your Entire Body

Finally, bring your attention to the sensations in your entire body. Allow yourself to notice the front, back, top, bottom, and sides of your body. Notice the wholeness of your body. Sense your breath moving through your entire body. Every inhalation invites you to sense your body, and every exhalation invites you to release any lingering tension from your entire body. Welcome yourself just as you are in this moment, without trying to change anything. Sense the deepest connection that resides within your heart. Sense how this deep connection allows you to reside within the peace that lives in the very core of your being. This is always here for you.

## Completion

Return your attention to your intention—the words that help you connect to a felt sense of connection, ease, and support. Once again, repeat this phrase to yourself two or three times. As you prepare to complete this practice, take a few moments to reflect on your experience. Slowly, when you are ready, begin to transition your full awareness back to your surroundings. If your eyes were closed, open them to notice the space around you. Bring your awareness to the sounds around you and to the sensation of the air on your skin. If you are lying down, slowly press back up into a comfortable sitting position. Take several breaths here, and when you are complete, notice what you are aware of now in your body, mind, emotions, and level of energy. Take some time to write down any observations, knowing that you can return to this practice as often as you would like.

_____

_____

_____

_____

_____

_____

_____

_____

_____

_____

_____

_____

_____

## Chapter Review

As you come to the conclusion of this chapter, I invite you to reflect on the invitation to connect to the softer side of yoga through loving-kindness, heart-opening, and restorative practices. When you explored letting go of your defenses, did any fears arise for you? What do you most long for when you imagine opening to love? How do you feel when you are invited to slow down and rest? If you would like, take some time to read your responses to the practices in this chapter. What are you taking away from this chapter? Are there any new tools that you would like to continue to explore as part of your personal yoga practice?

_____

_____

_____

_____

_____

_____

_____

_____

_____

_____

_____

_____

_____

_____

_____

## CHAPTER 5

# The Journey Is the Destination: Developing a Daily Practice

Within the previous four chapters, you have learned a wide range of therapeutic yoga practices for trauma recovery that can now be integrated to create a personalized practice. As you review the many practices offered in this book, you might wonder how to choose the poses or sequences that will best support you. Or you might find it difficult to commit to a personal practice. The purpose of this concluding chapter is to help you work through some of the common barriers that can interfere with any self-care routine and to provide you with guiding principles in developing a daily practice.

One of the characteristics associated with resilience after traumatic events is the commitment to staying involved and engaged with your life. By remaining dedicated to the healing process, you will see that the cumulative effect of your efforts helps you create positive changes. I invite you to recognize that a yoga practice can become a lifelong exploratory process that supports your journey of trauma recovery. Each practice offers you an opportunity for self-discovery, which allows you to awaken to new insights and awareness. In this way, the journey is the destination.

## Developing a Personalized Practice

Like any self-care routine, committing yourself to the practice of yoga is an act of honoring your body and mind. Therefore, if you are having difficulty committing to your personal practice, take some time to notice if you harbor any beliefs that are interfering with your ability to prioritize yourself. Perhaps you believe that you are not worthy of care or that you must take care of everyone else before you deserve to rest. Perhaps you find yourself avoiding embodiment practices because they evoke difficult emotions, such as shame or grief. These beliefs and emotions can sabotage your well-intended efforts to create space for yourself. You might even begin to notice an inner conflict that arises between the part of you who wants to engage in a regular yoga practice and the part of you who resists this process.

You might explore these inner conflicts and barriers in psychotherapy. Doing so can allow you to work through feelings of helplessness, fear, and shame or the inaccurate belief that nothing you do will make a difference. Having a co-regulating therapist can help you bring compassion and curiosity to your resistance, which facilitates a deeper understanding of the origin of your feelings and beliefs. Ideally, you will discover greater freedom that will help you commit to positive lifestyle changes.

It can also be beneficial to explore any additional supports that would help you successfully commit to your practice. For example, you might benefit from a therapeutic yoga instructor who can hold a compassionate space for your vulnerable feelings. Or you might find a friend who can serve as a practice partner. Alternatively, you might benefit from attending a group therapeutic yoga class with others who are in the trauma recovery process. Attending this type of group class offers you an opportunity to develop meaningful connections and reminds you that you are not alone with your struggles. The relationships and environment that surround your yoga practice can become a valuable component of the healing process.

Another practical way to develop a successful yoga routine is to discover the best time of the day or week that supports your practice. Committing to a certain practice time can help you develop regularity. You might notice that your needs vary depending on whether you are practicing in the morning, afternoon, or evening. Since your level of energy typically waxes and wanes with your circadian rhythm, you might notice that an active or empowering practice feels natural earlier in the day, whereas a restorative practice feels better when your energy dips in the midafternoon. You might also choose to start with shorter practice times of five or ten minutes a day. As you feel more comfortable with your practice, you might build up to thirty minutes or longer. Self-acceptance for the natural ebbs and flows of your energy will help you determine which practices from this book will best serve you at different times.

Even with a regular practice time, your needs will likely be different from day to day, depending on the degree of stress in your current circumstances, how you slept the night before, and whether you are dealing with any pain or illness symptoms. Some days you might prefer an energizing practice on your yoga mat, whereas other days you might prefer a gentle practice while seated in a chair. The length of time that you choose to spend in practice may also vary depending on your energy level or life demands.

## Guiding Principles

Once you are ready to step onto your yoga mat, I suggest structuring your practice using the following core components of therapeutic yoga for trauma recovery: orienting and centering, intention setting, conscious breathing, vagus nerve stimulation, warming up the body, mindfulness in movement, mindfulness in meditation, and integrative rest. Any given practice might have some or all of these components, and you can vary their order. The most important element for sustaining a daily practice is to find sufficient joy and reward as you deepen into your embodiment journey. Rather than pushing yourself into a practice, see if you can find a sense of effortlessness within your approach so even the strength-building poses feel nourishing for your body and any challenging emotional moments feel healing for your soul.

# Personalize Your Practice

Following are some suggestions for how you might integrate the various practices offered throughout this book to support your physical, mental, emotional, and spiritual well-being. Keep in mind that your practice needs will likely vary from day to day.

### Orienting and Centering

It is often beneficial to begin every practice with a few moments of self-observation, which will allow you to notice your body, mind, emotions, breath, and level of energy (see practice 4, *Orienting and Centering*). Once you are aware of your internal landscape, you can better determine whether you would benefit from an energizing or restorative practice.

### Intention Setting

Take a few moments to set an intention for your practice, which will help to support your growth (see practice 3, *Intention Setting*). This word or short phrase will focus your mind and give meaning to your practice. Perhaps your word reflects something that you are ready to change, let go of, or cultivate more of in your life at this time. What would help you to become the best version of yourself?

### Conscious Breathing

Choose a conscious-breathing practice that supports your physical, mental, and emotional needs. If you are feeling anxious or restless, you might choose *Three-Part Breath* (practice 6), *Balanced Breath* (practice 9), *Straw Breath* (practice 10), *Honeybee Breath* (practice 11), *Alternate Nostril Breathing* (practice 16), or *Cooling Breath* (practice 17). Alternatively, if you are in the midst of strong feelings, it can sometimes be beneficial to match this intensity by exploring *Warming Breath* or *Breath of Fire* (practice 17) before you practice a breath aimed to reduce sympathetic activation. In this way, you can learn to upregulate or downregulate your nervous system.

## Vagus Nerve Stimulation

Stimulating your vagus nerve toward the beginning of your practice can increase your sense of presence in the here and now. You can integrate some or all of the components from *Cultivate Sensory Awareness* (practice 12) and *Nourish Your Nervous System* (practice 13).

## Warming Up the Body

If you are engaging in physical postures, it is often beneficial to warm up with *Fluid Movements for a Flexible Spine* (practice 14), *Flow for Your Fascia* (practice 18), or *Spiral Movements to Unwind Stress* (practice 19). Doing so might help you notice if you are carrying any physical or emotional tension. This process helps initiate a conversation between your body and mind in which you listen to your sensations and allow them to guide intuitive movements.

## Mindfulness in Movement

At this point, you might choose to integrate additional movement practices. If you are wanting an energizing and empowering practice, you might return to *Steadiness and Strength* (practice 5) or to *Awaken Instinct and Intuition, Connect to Your Core,* or *Grounding Flow* (practices 20–22). If you are hoping to connect to an inner sense of flow, you might turn to *Root to Rise, Moving Meditation, Bowing to the Unknown,* or *Heart Opening* (practices 24–27). Or, if what you need is to slow down and settle your nervous system, you might prefer to revisit *Turning Inward* (practice 28). You might find that your body and mind thrive from an integrative practice that includes energizing movements followed by restorative postures.

## Mindfulness in Meditation

Mindful meditation can be added to your practice as a complement to the active elements of conscious breathing and movement. The breath and movement practices can often help your mind settle into the stillness of meditation.

However, you might also like to include a seated meditation at the beginning of your practice. To support your meditation practice, you might revisit *Awaken the Witness* (practice 8), *Self-Compassion* (practice 15), or *Loving-Kindness Meditation* (practice 23).

## Integrative Rest

Finally, explore a gentle shavasana for several minutes, or engage in the yoga nidra offering from *A Restorative Reset* (practice 29). You might choose to record the practice for yourself or ask someone whose voice you find soothing to record this practice for you, as this will allow you to effortlessly receive the benefits of the guided relaxation.

# Conclusion

Like a mosaic, it is always the small pieces that make up the big picture in a yoga practice. Each time you step on your yoga mat, you combine a variety of breath, movement, and body-awareness practices that facilitate your growth and help you create meaningful change. Collectively, they allow you to evolve into a bigger picture that is the ongoing creation of your life. My greatest hope is that the words and guided practices in this book have helped you access your embodied wisdom and strengthen your connection to your deepest self—that this journey to the heart has invited you to soften and let go of your defenses so you can more easily align with your true nature of kindness, generosity, love, and compassion.

As you continue on this journey, you might even discover a natural inclination to pay it forward through a genuine and heartfelt desire to show up in a caring and authentic manner with others. This is where your own personal healing journey extends beyond the yoga mat and intersects with the world. This loving exchange of giving and receiving is like an infinity symbol that reminds you that your own personal healing is deeply intertwined with the well-being of others.

As we conclude this book—this path we have shared for a time in our personal healing journeys—I bring my hands to my heart and bow. The light within me honors and recognizes the light within you.

*Namaste.*

# Guidelines for Therapists and Therapeutic Yoga Teachers

This section provides suggestions for therapists and yoga teachers on how to design a sequence of postures for an individual client or student. Within this section, you will also find a structure for how to create a six-week therapeutic yoga class.

When offering any therapeutic yoga practice, it is important to ensure that participants know they have a choice about whether or not they want to engage in the practice. Make sure they understand that they can say no and opt out of any practice. It is equally important to let participants know that they can adapt or change any practice. For example, they can choose to practice with their eyes open or closed, and they can choose to be seated in a chair or stand up. This emphasis on choice is especially important when offering any meditation or relaxation practice, since resting in stillness can feel very vulnerable for those who have an extended trauma history or who have a tendency toward dissociation and immobilization.

## Establishing Safety and Stabilization

When beginning your work with a client or student, I suggest moving slowly by introducing one practice at a time as you invite them to mindfully observe and share about their experience. It is wise to first assess for any potential concerns about their safety and self-care, and if they are engaging in any self-injurious behaviors (e.g., self-harm, suicidal thinking, addictive behaviors, disordered eating), focus on achieving stabilization prior to engaging in yogic interventions. Individuals who are actively engaged in any of the previous behaviors should receive psychotherapeutic support to develop greater safety and stability prior to engaging in the yoga interventions. Invite them to recognize that this process is the first step in a yoga practice, as it will allow them to refine their thoughts and behaviors so they can progress safely.

Eventually, this will provide a foundation that will help them create a yoga practice that recognizes their needs, honors their limitations, and is rooted in a foundation of kindness. Especially when working with individuals in the context of a six-week therapeutic yoga class, I suggest that they be in trauma-informed psychotherapy. When they are ready, you can work with them to create a personalized therapeutic yoga routine based on the practices in this book.

## Cultivating Neuroceptive Awareness and Co-regulation

When working with individuals who have experienced trauma, it is valuable to pay close attention to their window of tolerance as you offer therapeutic yoga interventions. Helping them cultivate *neuroceptive awareness*—an awareness of their internal cues of threat or safety—is particularly beneficial, as this will help them discern when they are above their window (e.g., anxious, agitated, overwhelmed), below their window (e.g., fatigued, disconnected, numb), or within their optimal zone of relaxed alertness. You can think of this as the "Goldilocks principle" discussed in chapter 2 as you assist clients to find their inner calm. With practice, you can also help clients increase their ability to effectively respond to a greater range of emotions and sensations.

Sometimes a client or student will feel frightened by the feelings that arise during a therapeutic yoga intervention. They might report that they feel nauseous or dizzy, or they might develop a slight headache. These somatic symptoms are a sign to slow down so the individual can integrate their embodied wisdom a little bit at a time. Sometimes somatic distress is a cue that the client has underlying emotions that are unexpressed. Often, pausing the practice, checking in with the individual, and allowing them to share about their experience is sufficient to help them integrate their experience. If they feel tired, you can honor the fatigue by encouraging them to rest. If they feel frozen or seem dissociated, you can invite them to orient to their sensory experience of the room by looking around and naming what they observe. You can also suggest that they wiggle their fingers and toes, squeeze their hands together, or press their feet firmly into the floor to help them mindfully move and connect to a felt sense of safety.

If your client or student reports any strong emotional reactions within a yogic intervention, it is important to recognize that these emotions and feeling states were already present within them. The yogic practice did not cause these reactions. Rather, the practice released some of their somatic armoring, and as a result, they accessed a felt sense of self that had previously been shielded from their conscious awareness. It is a profound gift when you can offer your presence during these moments.

As you remain unafraid of the client or student's emotions, they will relax. This will also reduce the likelihood that they will feel shame about their experience. Individuals who have experienced relational trauma may have never had another person who was able to be with them in their anger, fear, or sadness. They may carry attachment wounds of betrayal and abandonment. Your willingness to remain present with their pain is in alignment with the very essence of yoga. In contrast, some individuals may rely heavily on thinking during yoga interventions. This signals an intellectualization defense that may have been important at one time in their life as a means of self-protection. When this occurs, offer them your curiosity and acceptance while inviting them to do the same.

There may also be times when a client or student reports feeling numb, in which case rooting your own awareness in your legs and feet can help you remain grounded, which can provide a valuable counterbalance to their experience. This reflects the value of co-regulation, in which your capacity to be in a ventral vagal state offers a calm, compassionate, and regulating presence for another. Your capacity to offer care in a consistent, predictable, and trustworthy manner creates safety for someone else.

Importantly, your own personal yoga practice assists with your ability to co-regulate with others. Your ability to attune to your own body during a session or class will allow you to sense subtle changes that provide insight into the experience of another. For example, you might notice changes in how you are breathing, a feeling of pressure in your chest, or a catch in your throat. Your own awareness will then allow you to self-regulate by placing a hand over your heart or by taking a longer, slower breath. Not only does this allow you to model your own self-regulation, but it can offer a nonverbal invitation for the client or student to breathe more deeply.

Although it is normal to sometimes feel scared, sad, or worried about your client or student when they are in distress, if you are highly empathic, you might be particularly prone to feeling their pain. When this occurs, returning to your own self-care, breath, and awareness can help you navigate these moments so you can remain compassionate without feeling drained or fatigued. Remember, compassion is not driven by a need to fix another. Notice if you have an urge to rescue a student or client from their pain. In doing so, you might inadvertently interfere with the satisfaction that comes when they work through a challenge to arrive at a new insight. When you hold space for their process in a caring and warm manner, you honor their capacity to experience their own suffering and trust in their intrinsic wisdom, which will guide their path to resolution. This can lead them to discover a new felt sense of empowerment.

The following guidelines will help you navigate times when a client or student appears or reports feeling overwhelmed.

# What to Do When a Client or Student Feels Overwhelmed

### Assess

Explore with the student or client how they feel about what is occurring in this moment. Can they handle their feelings and sensations? Do you feel overwhelmed or do they? In general, it is helpful to focus on your own breathing and sense of being grounded so you can be a beneficial presence for another.

### Reflect

Express your willingness to be present with the client or student. You might say, "I see you have a lot of feelings right now. Your feelings are welcome here, and I'm here to support you." This might be sufficient to help them integrate their experience as they restore a sense of safety and connection.

### Intervene

If the client or student remains in distress, explore the following possible interventions:

- **Emotional Space:** "Would you like more interaction or more room to simply be with your experience?"
- **Proximity:** "Would you like me to be closer or farther away?"
- **Orienting:** "Look around the space. What do you see that reminds you that you are safe here and now? Can you hear the sound of my voice? Can you feel the air on your skin?"
- **Mobilizing:** "Notice how it feels to wiggle your fingers and toes. If you'd like, let's stand up and walk slowly around the room."
- **Grounding:** "If you'd like, let's stand up together and feel the strength of your legs as you press your feet firmly into the ground."
- **Boundary Setting:** "If you'd like, let's stand up together and press your hands into a wall. Feel the power of your push."

- **Breathing:** "If you feel comfortable, try to take several long, slow exhalations." (You might offer practice 10, *Straw Breath*, to help regulate the individual with the breath.)
- **Imagined Resource:** "Take a moment to reflect on a time when you felt connected to yourself in a meaningful way. Where were you? Who helped you developed this deep sense of connection to yourself? How do you feel in your body as you recall this time, place, or supportive person? Allow the image of this place, time, or person to help you return to a peaceful felt sense of connection, ease, and support."

## Leading an Individual Yoga Therapy Session

The following guidelines aim to support therapists and yoga teachers in creating a therapeutic yoga session with individual clients. Initially, you can guide the client or student through these practices during a session, but you can then encourage them to repeat the practice at home. Some practices are more easily integrated into psychotherapy sessions that involve being seated in a chair, whereas others are better are suited for yoga therapy sessions that involve using a yoga mat.

# An Individual Yoga Therapy Session

### Orienting and Centering

Discuss with your client or student the importance of developing awareness of their body, mind, breath, and nervous system cues. Together, you will explore whether they are experiencing sympathetic arousal in the form of a freeze, fight, or flight. Alternatively, you can assess if they are in a parasympathetic state in which they feel collapsed, shut down, or depressed. Guide the client to identify cues that suggest that they are safe now, which can allow them to arrive more fully for the session.

### Intention Setting

Discuss their goals for the therapeutic yoga session. For example, are they seeking to reduce anxiety, find relief from depression, improve their sleep, seek support for physical health concerns, or enhance self-compassion? Help them develop an intention that will support their practice (*Intention Setting*, practice 3).

### Conscious Breathing

Invite your client or student to experiment with a pranayama practice to help balance and support any emotional or nervous system activation. I suggest starting with the *Three-Part Breath* (practice 6) or *Balanced Breath* (practice 9). If they are feeling anxious or restless, you might choose to introduce *Straw Breath* (practice 10), *Honeybee Breath* (practice 11), *Alternate Nostril Breathing* (practice 16) or *Cooling Breath* (practice 17). Alternatively, if they are seeking an energizing and dynamic experience, you might explore *Warming Breath* or *Breath of Fire* (practice 17). In this way, you can help them learn to upregulate or downregulate their nervous system.

### Vagus Nerve Stimulation

Guide your client or student into part or all of the vagus nerve stimulation practices from *Cultivate Sensory Awareness* and *Nourish Your Nervous System* (practices 12 and 13). Progress slowly enough to allow them to notice and share any subtle shifts in response to the practice.

## Warming Up the Body

If your client or student will be engaging in physical postures, it is often beneficial to warm up with *Fluid Movements for a Flexible Spine* (practice 14), *Flow for Your Fascia* (practice 18), or *Spiral Movements to Unwind Stress* (practice 19). Doing so might help them notice if they are carrying any physical or emotional tension. This process will help the two of you refine how you will proceed with the session and will guide you both as you choose mindful movement practices.

## Mindfulness in Movement

If you are going to integrate yoga into a psychotherapy session, I suggest you start by inviting your client to slowly explore spinal movements while seated or standing to help them sense the connection between their posture, thoughts, and emotions. Doing so might help them notice if they are carrying any physical or emotional tension. From here, you might introduce yoga postures that feel relevant to the client's intention. For example, you can offer mountain and tree poses to help them feel rooted and balanced in the midst of a stressful time. You can invite them to explore warrior two or five-pointed star to help them find their inner strength and courage when facing a challenge. Or you might invite them to settle into a seated child's pose over a pillow to create a felt sense of comfort amid vulnerable feelings.

If you are offering a mat-based practice, you might be able to explore a wider range of postures and practices. For example, you might explore an energizing and empowering practice with *Awaken Instinct and Intuition, Connect to Your Core*, or *Grounding Flow* (practices 20–22). If the client or student is seeking to connect to an inner sense of ease and balance, you might introduce *Root to Rise, Moving Meditation, Bowing to the Unknown*, or *Heart Opening* (practices 24–27). Or, if what they are needing is to settle into a felt sense of safety, you might prefer to revisit *Turning Inward* (practice 28). Once a client or student gains comfort with the range of practices, you can help them create an integrative practice that includes energizing movements followed by restorative postures.

## Mindfulness in Meditation

Depending on the need and interest of the client or student, you might guide them through one of the mindfulness practices. *Awaken the Witness* (practice 8) focuses on nonjudgmentally observing thoughts, *Self-Compassion* (practice 15) focuses on increasing a feeling of warmth and self-acceptance, and *Loving-Kindness Meditation* (practice 23) extends this compassion outward toward others. You may choose to introduce this practice toward the beginning of the practice, depending on the individual needs of your client.

## Integrative Rest

Explore inviting your client or student to experience part or all of the guided yoga nidra offering from *A Restorative Reset* (practice 29). In order to enhance a sense of safety in the practice, they can choose to remain seated or lying down, and they can keep their eyes open or closed.

# Leading a Group Yoga Therapy Session

If you are planning on teaching a group therapeutic yoga class, the following structure can get you started. It is helpful to limit the class size to about six to eight students, which will allow you to develop sufficient connection and safety between you and the class members. With a small enough group of students, you will have an opportunity to observe each individual's movement and level of energy so you can adapt or tailor the class to meet their needs. Typically, ninety minutes will provide enough time for the class. As previously discussed, you can invite each student to discover their own window of tolerance and encourage them to follow a pace that honors their body and mind. Let them know that while this is a group class, they will often be moving their bodies quite differently. Encourage them to draw their attention inward and to listen to their sensations as a guide for their movements.

When done in a group format, therapeutic yoga for trauma recovery encourages a deepening of connection between the students. Each class begins with all of the students sitting in a circle while the teacher offers a brief psychoeducational teaching that identifies the theme for the class. Ideally, this brief talk takes about five to ten minutes and concludes with a specific question or statement that helps structure the check-in process. During the check-in, invite each student to share with the group their thoughts about, or an experience related to, the class theme. However, make sure to let students know that this check-in is optional.

When checking in, it is helpful to ask each student to limit their sharing to about two minutes and to complete their sharing by identifying a specific intention for that day's practice. The sharing circle allows group members to repair wounds of not belonging, feeling exiled, or feeling excluded. This process recognizes that our wounds do not happen in a vacuum; therefore, trauma needs repaired interpersonally within a safe community. Importantly, the group norm is that members simply respond to each person's sharing by saying "thank you." Responses that involve personal reactions, feedback, or "helpful" advice are strongly discouraged.

Upon completion of the sharing circle, invite each student to return to their yoga mat and to settle into any shape that helps them draw their awareness back to themselves. I offer that they might choose to remain seated or settle into any resting shape that feels supportive to them. Remind them that they can keep their eyes open or closed as they orient to their experience of the group, the room, and their body. After several minutes, invite students into the breath, movement, and body-awareness practices that support the theme for that class. Offer each practice with invitational language, making sure to include periodic reminders that students may choose to opt out or rest at any time.

The sequence of asana and pranayama typically lasts for about forty-five minutes and is followed by a guided meditation or relaxation practice that facilitate integrations of the practice. The class ends with an invitation for the students to return to sitting in a circle. This time, invite each student to briefly share anything that they noticed as a result of the class. This final opportunity to share as a group allows you to observe students before they leave the room and to intervene if anyone is feeling vulnerable as a result of the practice.

I suggest structuring the yoga class as a six-week series, which encourages the same group of students to return each week. This allows the group to begin to feel familiar and helps students feel connected to each other. Having taught this model for many years, I have found that students often return and repeat the initial series of classes to strengthen their skills. It can also be helpful to offer a "continuing" class for students who have already taken the introductory six-week class and are ready to deepen their practice. You might find that the continuing class can accommodate a larger group size, since the students have developed a greater capacity to self-regulate through a wider range of emotions and nervous system states.

Each class in the six-week series offers the following core components of therapeutic yoga for trauma recovery: psychoeducation, sharing prompt, orienting and centering, conscious breathing, vagus nerve stimulation, warming up the body, mindfulness in meditation, mindfulness in movement, and integrative rest. Importantly, you might adapt the themes, modify the sharing prompts, and add or delete practices so they feel relevant to the unique needs of your students.

# A Six-Week Series of Therapeutic Yoga for Trauma Recovery

This is a sample six-week course of yoga for trauma recovery. You may adapt this model to meet the needs of your students.

## Week 1: Choice and Freedom

The purpose of the first class is to help your students to find a sense of safety in their bodies. You will guide them through a dual awareness practice to increase their capacity to be with their emotions and sensations without becoming overwhelmed. The practices chosen for this class emphasize a willful practice that will help your students to feel strong and empowered in their bodies.

- **Psychoeducation:** Discuss the connection between a felt sense of safety and having choice (see *The Freedom to Choose* in chapter 1). Introduce the concept of setting an intention (see *Limb 1: Seeds of Change* in chapter 1). Describe how they can build the capacity for dual awareness to enhance cues of safety in the here and now (see *Limbs 5 and 6: Dual Awareness and Trauma Recovery* in chapter 1).

- **Sharing Prompt:** Ask the group, "Why did you sign up for this class? What are you hoping to get out of these classes overall? What is your intention for today?"

- **Orienting and Centering:** Introduce practice 4, *Orienting and Centering*, to help the students observe cues from their body and mind that suggest that they are in a defensive state. They can also identify cues that suggest that they are safe now, which can allow them to arrive more fully for the class.

- **Mindfulness in Meditation:** Guide the students in a seated dual awareness practice that invites them to alternate paying attention to external cues of safety and their internal experience of physical sensations or emotions. You can draw upon the dual awareness guided practices found in *Resting in Child's Pose* (practice 7).

- **Conscious Breathing:** Guide the students into the yogic *Three-Part Breath* (practice 6) to enhance a relaxation response.
- **Vagus Nerve Stimulation:** Guide your students through *Cultivate Sensory Awareness* (practice 12). Progress slowly enough to allow the students to notice any subtle shifts in response to each element of the practice.
- **Warming Up the Body:** To help your students warm up the spine, lead them through *Fluid Movements for a Flexible Spine* (practice 14) while seated on the yoga mat or in a chair. Then encourage them to explore this practice while standing in preparation for the next series of standing postures.
- **Mindfulness in Movement:** Introduce the students to a gentle standing moving flow with *Steadiness and Strength* (practice 5), followed by tree pose with *Root to Rise* (practice 24). Complete the movement sequence with *Resting in Child's Pose* (practice 7). Periodically remind your students that they can integrate dual awareness strategies throughout the practice.
- **Integrative Rest:** Invite the students to take a gentle shavasana for several minutes to conclude the class.

### Week 2: Awaken the Witness

This second class guides the students to nonjudgmentally observe their thoughts, emotions, and sensations as you introduce eye movements, gentle stretches aimed to release tension in the neck, and pandicular movement. These practices can evoke vulnerable emotions, so it is important to progress slowly, which will help the students integrate and digest any new awareness. This class then revisits the willful practices from the previous week to strengthen the students' embodied resource of empowerment.

- **Psychoeducation:** Discuss the value of cultivating a nonjudgmental witness (see *Limbs 7 and 8: The Wisdom of Pure Awareness* in chapter 1).
- **Sharing Prompt:** Ask the group, "In what ways have the events from your past led you to develop inaccurate or hurtful beliefs

about yourself? What would you like to believe about yourself now? What is your intention for today that aligns with this positive belief?"

- **Orienting and Centering:** Offer an abbreviated version *Orienting and Centering* (practice 4), which allows the students to become aware of their body sensations, thoughts, emotions, and breath.
- **Mindfulness in Meditation:** Guide the class through *Awaken the Witness* (practice 8) to allow each member to connect with the wisdom of their true self.
- **Conscious Breathing:** Teach *Balanced Breath* (practice 9) to help your students generate inner feelings of relaxation, contentment, and balance.
- **Vagus Nerve Stimulation:** Guide the students through *Nourish Your Nervous System* (practice 13). Progress slowly enough to allow the students to notice any subtle shifts in response to each element of the practice.
- **Warming Up the Body:** From a seated position, lead your students through *Fluid Movements for a Flexible Spine* (practice 14) to help them warm up the spine, followed by *Flow for Your Fascia* (practice 18) to increase sensory awareness through natural movements. Then encourage them to explore *Fluid Movements for a Flexible Spine* while standing in preparation for the next series of standing postures.
- **Mindfulness in Movement:** Revisit the gentle standing moving flow with *Steadiness and Strength* (practice 5), followed by tree pose with *Root to Rise* (practice 24). Complete the movement sequence with *Resting in Child's Pose* (practice 7).
- **Integrative Rest:** Invite the students to take a gentle shavasana for several minutes to conclude the class.

### Week 3: Cultivate Equanimity

In the third class, you will teach your students about polyvagal theory as applied to yoga by introducing the three states of the nervous system through the Goldilocks metaphor. The breathing practices chosen for this week aim to facilitate greater balance in the nervous system, while the mindful movements focus on releasing stress through unwinding the fascia. Once again, you will guide the students through willful practices to strengthen their embodied resources. This week, you will conclude the class by guiding your students through a seated self-compassion practice after a brief integrative rest.

- **Psychoeducation:** Discuss polyvagal theory and how the three nervous system states mirror the three gunas: rajas, tamas, and sattva (see *Equanimity Amid Change* in chapter 2). Share the Goldilocks metaphor.

- **Sharing Prompt:** Ask the group, "Are there times when you have felt restless, anxious, or excessively angry? Can you think of times when you have felt dull, lethargic, fatigued, or depressed? Perhaps you struggle with energetic imbalances in either direction. If so, what has helped you find a sense of balance?"

- **Orienting and Centering:** Offer an abbreviated version of *Orienting and Centering* (practice 4), guiding your students to develop awareness of their body sensations, state of mind, emotions, breath, and level of energy.

- **Conscious Breathing:** Guide your students through *Straw Breath* (practice 10) to help induce a parasympathetic response.

- **Vagus Nerve Stimulation:** Guide your students through *Honeybee Breath* (practice 11) to activate the vagus nerve.

- **Warming Up the Body:** From a seated position, lead the students through *Fluid Movements for a Flexible Spine* (practice 14), followed by *Flow for Your Fascia* (practice 18). Then invite them to explore *Fluid Movements for a Flexible Spine* while standing in preparation for *Spiral Movements to Unwind Stress* (practice 19).

- **Mindfulness in Movement:** Introduce *Awaken Instinct and Intuition* (practice 20). Then revisit the gentle standing moving flow with *Steadiness and Strength* (practice 5), followed by tree pose with *Root to Rise* (practice 24). Complete the movement sequence with *Resting in Child's Pose* (practice 7).

- **Integrative Rest:** Invite the students to sit or lie down in a gentle shavasana for several minutes.
- **Mindfulness in Meditation:** One of the purposes of yoga is to prepare the students for seated meditation. Therefore, conclude this class with *Self-Compassion* (practice 15) to help them learn to hold themselves in a loving and kind way.

### Week 4: Embodiment as Empowerment

The purpose of the fourth class is to engage in practices that safely mobilize and upregulate the body and mind. The conscious breathing practices this week are warming and energizing, while the mindful movement practices focus on strengthening the core and grounding through the legs. Encourage your students to pay attention to the feedback they are getting from their bodies so they can wisely choose whether or not to engage in these practices, which are aimed to enhance their felt sense of vitality. This practice concludes with a cooling breath and a brief seated meditation.

- **Psychoeducation:** Discuss how trauma can impact the body and how we can access the healing power of the body through instinctual, empowering, and grounding movements (see the *Repatterning Your Body*, *Embodiment as Empowerment*, and *Enhance Your Vitality* sections in chapter 3).
- **Sharing Prompt:** Ask the group, "How have difficult or traumatic experiences led you to develop tension patterns in your body, your posture, your breath, or your movements? Remember, your body is wise. Even though the effects of traumatic events are painful, see if you can identify how these defensive responses may have been important at some point in your life. How did they help you survive?"
- **Orienting and Centering:** Offer an abbreviated version of *Orienting and Centering* (practice 4), guiding your students to develop awareness of their body sensations, state of mind, emotions, breath, and level of energy.

- **Conscious Breathing:** Revisit *Balanced Breath* (practice 9). Then introduce *Warming Breath* and *Breath of Fire* (practice 17). Remind your students that these practices are optional and that they can stay with *Balanced Breath* if they choose.
- **Vagus Nerve Stimulation:** Guide your students through *Cultivate Sensory Awareness* (practice 12). Progress slowly enough to allow the students to notice any subtle shifts in response to each element of the practice.
- **Warm Up the Body:** From a seated position, lead students through *Fluid Movements for a Flexible Spine* (practice 14) to help them warm up the spine, followed by *Flow for Your Fascia* (practice 18) to increase sensory awareness through natural movements.
- **Mindfulness in Movement:** Revisit *Awaken Instinct and Intuition* (practice 20), and then introduce *Connect to Your Core* and *Grounding Flow* (practices 21 and 22).
- **Integrative Rest:** The previous *Grounding Flow* practice ends with a reclined bound angle pose, in which you invite the students to lie down on their backs and bend their knees to bring the soles of their feet together. You can invite your students to remain in this shape or to extend their legs long for a traditional shavasana for several minutes.
- **Conscious Breathing:** Invite the students to return to a seated posture for a final pranayama to help close this practice. Introduce the *Cooling Breath* (practice 17). Upon completion of these energizing practices, the cooling breath reengages the parasympathetic nervous system to slow down the body and mind in preparation for a brief seated meditation practice.
- **Mindfulness in Meditation:** Since one of the purposes of yoga is to prepare the students for seated meditation, we conclude this class by revisiting *Awaken the Witness* (practice 8), which will help the students observe subtle changes in body and mind that arose as a result of the practice.

## Week 5: Brain and Body Integration

The fifth class teaches the students about the impact of trauma on the body and mind and the value of contralateral movements to facilitate greater brain integration. If your students feel ready to deepen their process, they are invited to focus their intention for class by identifying one area of difficulty from their past or present that feels unresolved. The conscious breathing and mindful movements this week strengthen the students' connection to their intuition and inner strength. Finally, restorative postures facilitate an inward turn in preparation for the closing meditation practice.

- **Psychoeducation:** Discuss the impact of trauma on the brain (see *Brain and Body Integration* from chapter 3). Share how cross-lateral movements, breath practices, and somatic awareness helps us access our "wise mind" and a coherent nervous system state, which allows us to make decisions, handle conflicts, and respond to stress. Introduce the yogic concept of ida and pingala nadis as representative of the polarities of the lunar and solar aspects of self. Share about the sushumna nadi and how connecting to their center facilitates an easeful or peaceful mind.

- **Sharing Prompt:** Explain to the group, "It is human instinct to avoid pain, but in time, you can build the courage to turn toward your difficult feelings and memories. Of course, it is important to do so at a pace that you can tolerate. Today, I invite you to share one area of difficulty that is either currently in your life or an experience from your past. Can you set an intention about how you would like to feel once this area of difficulty is resolved?"

- **Orienting and Centering:** Offer an abbreviated version of *Orienting and Centering* (practice 4), guiding your students to develop awareness of their body sensations, state of mind, emotions, breath, and level of energy.

- **Conscious Breathing:** Guide your students through *Alternate Nostril Breathing* (practice 16) to encourage integration across the right and left sides of the body.

- **Vagus Nerve Stimulation:** Guide your students through *Nourish Your Nervous System* (practice 13). Progress slowly enough to allow the students to notice any subtle shifts in response to each element of the practice.
- **Warming Up the Body:** From a seated position, lead the students through *Fluid Movements for a Flexible Spine* (practice 14) to help them warm up the spine, followed by *Flow for Your Fascia* (practice 18) to increase sensory awareness through natural movements.
- **Mindfulness in Movement:** Revisit *Awaken Instinct and Intuition* (practice 20) and *Connect to Your Core* (practice 21). Introduce *Moving Meditation* (practice 25) to help your students cultivate a sense of flow and mastery, and then guide them through *Turning Inward* (practice 28) to help them release tension.
- **Integrative Rest:** End the *Turning Inward* practice with a legs-up-the-wall pose, inviting your students to extend their legs long for several minutes to integrate the asana portion of the class.
- **Mindfulness in Meditation:** Finish the class by revisiting *Self-Compassion* (practice 15) with a specific focus on the area of difficulty that each student identified at the beginning of the practice. Invite your students to notice what has changed as a result of the practice. If there is any lingering distress, invite them to direct self-compassion toward this area of difficulty.

### Week 6: Opening to Love

The final class focuses on connecting to the heart and invites a deepening of emotional sharing, with an understanding that this six-week series is coming to a close. The practices in this sequence are chosen because they facilitate a gentle and safe opening of the heart while helping the students discover an inward turn and softening of muscular tension. This class concludes with a guided yoga nidra and a seated loving-kindness meditation. Often, students have developed a bond and a felt sense of safety with each other, so they may need extra time for closure in the final sharing circle prior to saying goodbye.

- **Psychoeducation:** Discuss the healing properties of heart-opening and restorative practices (see *Opening to Love*, *The Soft Side of Yoga*, and *Settling into Stillness* from chapter 4). Heart-opening practices are an invitation to move beyond the reactivity of defensive states of fight or flight. To open the heart and soften the body involves letting down our armor and surrendering our vigilance, which can be quite vulnerable. Introduce the loving-kindness meditation as a way to support this journey to the heart (see *A Path to Self-Realization* from chapter 4).

- **Sharing Prompt:** Ask the group, "What comes up for you when you think about opening your heart, softening your defenses, and slowing down? What messages did you learn about resting or taking time for yourself? What thoughts or feelings arise when you think about letting go of your defenses? What are your deepest longings and hopes when you imagine softening your defenses and opening your heart? How can this inform your intention for today?"

- **Orienting and Centering:** Offer an abbreviated version of *Orienting and Centering* (practice 4), guiding your students to develop awareness of their body sensations, state of mind, emotions, breath, and level of energy.

- **Conscious Breathing:** Guide your students through the yogic *Three-Part Breath* (practice 6) to enhance a relaxation response.

- **Vagus Nerve Stimulation:** Revisit *Honeybee Breath* (practice 11) to activate the vagus nerve.

- **Warming Up the Body:** From a seated position, lead the students through *Fluid Movements for a Flexible Spine* (practice 14) to help them warm up the spine, followed by *Flow for Your Fascia* (practice 18) to increase sensory awareness through natural movements. Then explore *Fluid Movements for a Flexible Spine* while standing in preparation for *Spiral Movements to Unwind Stress* (practice 19).

- **Mindfulness in Movement:** Revisit *Moving Meditation* (practice 25), and then introduce *Bowing to the Unknown* and *Heart Opening* (practices 26 and 27). Complete the movement exploration by revisiting *Turning Inward* (practice 28). Collectively, this sequence of postures aims to safely and gently open the heart while allowing the students to remain humbly connected to the earth.

- **Integrative Rest:** Invite your students to extend their legs long for a guided yoga nidra using *A Restorative Reset* (practice 29). In order to enhance a sense of safety in the practice, the students can choose to remain seated or lying down, and they can keep their eyes open or closed.

- **Mindfulness in Meditation:** Return to a seated position, and introduce the *Loving-Kindness Meditation* (practice 23) to enhance the integration of the heart-opening practices from the class.

Most importantly, I want to remind you to trust yourself as a guide for your clients and students through the journey of therapeutic yoga for trauma recovery. It is often necessary to adapt a session or class sequence to meet the needs of those with whom you work. As you engage in the compassionate role as a co-regulating presence, you will know get to know your students, and together you will find your way. Remind your clients and students to listen to their bodies. Their ability to honor their truth is the most important part of the practice. My deepest hope is that you will allow your role as a therapeutic yoga teacher to be as nourishing to you as your presence will be for your students.

# References

For your convenience, purchasers can download and print
the worksheets from www.pesi.com/yogafortrauma

Abel, R., Jr. (2014). *The eye care revolution: Prevent and reverse common vision problems* (3rd ed.). Kensington Books.

Aposhyan, S. (2007). *Natural intelligence: Body-mind integration and human development.* NOW Press.

Armour, J. A. (2008). Potential clinical relevance of the "little brain" on the mammalian heart. *Experimental Physiology, 93*(2), 165–176. https://doi.org/10.1113/expphysiol.2007.041178

Bainbridge Cohen, B. (1994). *Sensing, feeling, and action: The experiential anatomy of body-mind centering.* Contact Editions.

Bayes, A., Tavella, G., & Parker, G. (2021). The biology of burnout: Causes and consequences. *The World Journal of Biological Psychiatry, 22*(9), 686–698. https://doi.org/10.1080/15622975.2021.1907713

Beauchaine, T. (2001). Vagal tone, development, and Gray's motivational theory: Toward an integrated model of autonomic nervous system functioning in psychopathology. *Development and Psychopathology, 13*(2), 183–214. https://doi.org/10.1017/s0954579401002012

Bennett, M. J., & Castiglioni, I. (2004). Embodied ethnocentrism and the feeling of culture: A key to training for intercultural competence. In D. Landis, J. Bennett, & M. Bennett (Eds.), *Handbook of intercultural training* (3rd ed., pp. 249–265). Sage.

Benson, H., & Proctor, W. (2011). *Relaxation revolution: The science and genetics of mind body healing.* Simon & Schuster.

Berceli, D. (2008). *The revolutionary trauma release process: Transcend your toughest times.* Namaste Publishing.

Berceli, D. (2015). *Shake it off naturally: Reduce stress, anxiety, and tension with (TRE).* CreateSpace.

Bergmann, U. (2008). The neurobiology of EMDR: Exploring the thalamus and neural integration. *Journal of EMDR Practice and Research, 2*(4), 300–314. http://dx.doi.org/10.1891/1933-3196.2.4.300

Brown, R. P., & Gerbarg, P. L. (2005a). Sudarshan Kriya yogic breathing in the treatment of stress, anxiety, and depression: Part I—neurophysiologic model. *Journal of Alternative & Complementary Medicine, 11*(1), 189–201. https://doi.org/10.1089/acm.2005.11.189

Brown, R. P., & Gerbarg, P. L. (2005b). Sudarshan Kriya Yogic breathing in the treatment of stress, anxiety, and depression: Part II—clinical applications and guidelines. *Journal of Alternative & Complementary Medicine, 11*(4), 711–717. https://doi.org/10.1089/acm.2005.11.711

Bulbena-Cabré, A., & Bulbena, A. (2018). Anxiety and joint hypermobility: An unexpected association. *Current Psychiatry, 17*(4), 15–21. http://www.sepsiq.org/file/InformacionSM/Current%20Psychiatry.pdf

Carney, D. R., Cuddy, A. J. C., & Yap, A. J. (2010). Power posing: Brief nonverbal displays affect neuroendocrine levels and risk tolerance. *Psychological Science, 21*(10), 1363–1368. https://doi.org/10.1177/0956797610383437

Carson, J. W., Keefe, F. J., Lynch, T. R., Carson, K. M., Goli, V., Fras, A. M., & Thorp, S. R. (2005). Loving-kindness meditation for chronic low back pain: Results from a pilot trial. *Journal of Holistic Nursing, 23*(3), 287–304. https://doi.org/10.1177%2F0898010105277651

Craig, A. D. (2010). The sentient self. *Brain Structure and Function, 214*(5–6), 563–577. https://doi.org/10.1007/s00429-010-0248-y

Csikszentmihalyi, M. (1990). *Flow: The psychology of optimal experience.* Harper Perennial.

Cuddy, A. J. C., Schultz, S. J., & Fosse, N. E. (2018). *P*-curving a more comprehensive body of research on postural feedback reveals clear evidential value for power-posing effects: Reply to Simmons and Simonsohn (2017). *Psychological Science, 29*(4), 656–666. https://doi.org/10.1177%2F0956797617746749

Damasio, A. (1999). *The feeling of what happens: Body and emotion in the making of consciousness.* Harcourt Brace.

Dana, D. A. (2018). *The polyvagal theory in therapy: Engaging the rhythm of regulation.* W. W. Norton.

Desai, R., Tailor, A., & Bhatt, T. (2015). Effects of yoga on brain waves and structural activation: A review. *Complementary Therapies in Clinical Practice, 21*(2), 112–118. https://doi.org/10.1016/j.ctcp.2015.02.002

Deuchars, S. A., Lall, V. K., Clancy, J., Mahadi, M., Murray, A., Peers, L., & Deuchars, J. (2018). Mechanisms underpinning sympathetic nervous activity and its modulation using transcutaneous vagus nerve stimulation. *Experimental Physiology, 103*(3), 326–331. https://dx.doi.org/10.1113%2FEP086433

de Voogd, L. D., Kanen, J. W., Neville, D. A., Roelofs, K., Fernández, G., & Hermans, E. J. (2018). Eye-movement intervention enhances extinction via amygdala deactivation. *The Journal of Neuroscience, 38*(40), 8694–8706. https://doi.org/10.1523/JNEUROSCI.0703-18.2018

Dorsher, P. T. (2009). Myofascial meridians as anatomical evidence of acupuncture channels. *Medical Acupuncture, 21*(2), 91–97. https://doi.org/10.1089/acu.2009.0631

Dreisoerner, A., Junker, N. M., Schlotz, W., Heimrich, J., Bloemeke, S., Ditzen, B., & van Dick, R. (2021). Self-soothing touch and being hugged reduce cortisol responses to stress: A randomized controlled trial on stress, physical touch, and social identity. *Comprehensive Psychoneuroendocrinology, 8*, Article 100091. https://doi.org/10.1016/j.cpnec.2021.100091

Emerson, D. (2015). *Trauma-sensitive yoga in therapy: Bringing the body into treatment.* W. W. Norton.

Emmons, R. A. (2007). Gratitude, subjective well-being, and the brain. In M. Eid & R. J. Larsen (Eds.), *The science of subjective well-being* (pp. 469–492). Guilford Press.

Emmons, R. A., & McCullough, M. E. (2003). Counting blessings versus burdens: An experimental investigation of gratitude and subjective well-being in daily life. *Journal of Personality and Social Psychology, 84*(2), 377–389. https://doi.org/10.1037//0022-3514.84.2.377

Fogel, A. (2009). *Body sense: The science and practice of embodied self-awareness.* W. W. Norton.

Gotink, R. A., Vernooij, M. W., Ikram, M. A., Niessen, W. J., Krestin, G. P., Hofman, A., Tiemeier, H., & Myriam Hunink, M. G. (2018). Meditation and yoga practice are associated with smaller right amygdala volume: The Rotterdam study. *Brain Imaging and Behavior, 12*(6), 1631–1639. https://doi.org/10.1007/s11682-018-9826-z

Hanh, T. N. (2014). *No mud, no lotus: The art of transforming suffering.* Parallax Press.

Hanna, T. (2004). *Somatics: Reawakening the mind's control of movement, flexibility, and health*. Da Capo.

Hannaford, C. (1995). *Smart moves: Why learning is not all in your head*. Great Ocean Publishers.

Hayes, S. C. (2005). *Get out of your mind and into your life: The new acceptance and commitment therapy*. New Harbinger Publications.

Hopwood, T. L., & Schutte, N. S. (2017). A meta-analytic investigation of the impact of mindfulness-based interventions on post traumatic stress. *Clinical Psychology Review, 57*, 12–20. https://doi.org/10.1016/j.cpr.2017.08.002

Insel, T. R. (2000). Toward a neurobiology of attachment. *Review of General Psychology, 4*(2), 176–185. https://doi.org/10.1037%2F1089-2680.4.2.176

Jean, A. D., & Stack, D. M. (2009). Functions of maternal touch and infants' affect during face-to-face interactions: New directions for the still-face. *Infant Behavior & Development, 32*(1), 123–128. https://doi.org/10.1016/j.infbeh.2008.09.008

Jovanov, E. (2005, September 1–4). *On spectral analysis of heart rate variability during very slow yogic breathing* [Paper presentation]. IEEE Engineering in Medicine and Biology Society 27th Annual Conference, Shanghai, China.

Khalsa, S. S., Adolphs, R., Cameron, O. G., Critchley, H. D., Davenport, P. W., Feinstein, J. S., Feusner, J. D., Garfinkel, S. N., Lane, R. D., Mehling, W. E., Meuret, A. E., Nemeroff, C. B., Oppenheimer, S., Petzschner, F. H., Pollatos, O., Rhudy, J. L., Schramm, L. P., Simmons, W. K., Stein, M. B., … the Interoception Summit 2016 participants. (2018). Interoception and mental health: A roadmap. *Biological Psychiatry, 3*(6), 501–513. https://doi.org/10.1016/j.bpsc.2017.12.004

Kimmel, M. (2013). The arc from the body to culture: How affect, proprioception, kinesthesia, and perceptual imagery shape cultural knowledge (and vice versa). *Integral Review, 9*(2), 300–348. https://integral-review.org/issues/vol_9_no_2_kimmel_the_arc_from_the_body_to_culture.pdf

Kok, B. E., Coffey, K. A., Cohn, M. A., Catalino, L. I., Vacharkulksemsuk, T., Algoe, S. B., Brantley, M., & Fredrickson, B. L. (2013). How positive emotions build physical health: Perceived positive social connections account for the upward spiral between positive emotions and vagal tone. *Psychological Science, 24*(7), 1123–1132. https://doi.org/10.1177%2F0956797612470827

Kok, B. E., & Fredrickson, B. L. (2010). Upward spirals of the heart: Autonomic flexibility, as indexed by vagal tone, reciprocally and prospectively predicts positive emotions and social connectedness. *Biological Psychology, 85*(3), 432–436. https://dx.doi.org/10.1016%2Fj.biopsycho.2010.09.005

Kozlowska, K., Walker, P., McLean, L., & Carrive, P. (2015). Fear and the defense cascade: Clinical implications and management. *Harvard Review of Psychiatry, 23*(4), 263–287. https://dx.doi.org/10.1097%2FHRP.0000000000000065

Larrivee, D., & Echarte, L. (2018). Contemplative meditation and neuroscience: Prospects for mental health. *Journal of Religion and Health, 57*(3), 960–978. https://doi.org/10.1007/s10943-017-0475-0

Levine, P. A. (2010). *In an unspoken voice: How the body releases trauma and restores goodness*. North Atlantic Books.

Lowen, A. (1977). *Bioenergetics: The revolutionary therapy that uses the language of the body to heal the problems of the mind*. Penguin.

Lutz, J. (2021). *Trauma healing in the yoga zone*. Handspring Publishing Limited.

Mahour, J., & Verma, P. (2017). Effect of ujjayi pranayama on cardiovascular autonomic function tests. *National Journal of Physiology, Pharmacy and Pharmacology, 7*(4), 391–395. https://www.njppp.com/fulltext/28-1476538333.pdf

Maslow, A. H. (1968). *Toward a psychology of being.* Van Nostrand.

Mathôt, S., & Van der Stigchel, S. (2015). New light on the mind's eye: The pupillary light response as active vision. *Current Directions in Psychological Science, 24*(5), 374–378. https://doi.org/10.1177/0963721415593725

Matthews, M. J., Yusuf, M., Doyle, C., & Thompson, C. (2016). Quadrupedal movement training improves markers of cognition and joint repositioning. *Human Movement Science, 47*, 70–80. https://doi.org/10.1016/j.humov.2016.02.002

McCraty, R. (2017). New frontiers in heart rate variability and social coherence research: Techniques, technologies, and implications for improving group dynamics and outcomes. *Frontiers in Public Health, 5*, Article 267. https://doi.org/10.3389/fpubh.2017.00267

Menakem, R. (2017). *My grandmother's hands: Racialized trauma and the pathway to mending our hearts and bodies.* Central Recovery Press.

Merleau-Ponty, M. (1962). *Phenomenology of perception.* Routledge and Kegan Paul.

Moszeik, E. N., von Oertzen, T., & Renner, K.-H. (2020). Effectiveness of a short Yoga Nidra meditation on stress, sleep, and well-being in a large and diverse sample. *Current Psychology,* 1–15. https://doi.org/10.1007/s12144-020-01042-2

Müller, V., & Lindenberger, U. (2011). Cardiac and respiratory patterns synchronize between persons during choir singing. *PloS One, 6*(9), Article e24893. https://doi.org/10.1371/journal.pone.0024893

Myers, T. W., & Hillman, S. K. (2004). *Anatomy trains.* Primal Pictures Limited.

Niklasson, M., Rasmussen, P., Niklasson, I., & Norlander, T. (2015). Adults with sensorimotor disorders: Enhanced physiological and psychological development following specific sensorimotor training. *Frontiers in Psychology, 6*, Article 480. https://doi.org/10.3389/fpsyg.2015.00480

Nivethitha, L., Manjunath, N. K., & Mooventhan, A. (2017). Heart rate variability changes during and after the practice of bhramari pranayama. *International Journal of Yoga, 10*(2), 99–102. https://doi.org/10.4103/0973-6131.205518

Ogden, P. (2009). Modulation, mindfulness, and movement in the treatment of trauma-related depression. In M. Kerman (Ed.), *Clinical pearls of wisdom: 21 leading therapists offer their key insights* (pp. 1–13). W. W. Norton.

Ogden, P., Minton, K., & Pain, C. (2006). *Trauma and the body: A sensorimotor approach to psychotherapy.* W. W. Norton.

Patañjali. (2003). *The yoga-sūtra of Patañjali: A new translation with commentary.* (C. Hartranft, Trans.). Shambhala Publications. (Original work published ca. 400 CE).

Payne, P., Levine, P. A., & Crane-Godreau, M. A. (2015). Somatic experiencing: Using interoception and proprioception as core elements of trauma therapy. *Frontiers in Psychology, 6*, Article 93. https://doi.org/10.3389/fpsyg.2015.00093

Pert, C. B. (1997). *Molecules of emotion: Why you feel the way you feel.* Simon & Schuster.

Pinna, T., & Edwards, D. J. (2020). A systematic review of associations between interoception, vagal tone, and emotional regulation: Potential applications for mental health, wellbeing, psychological flexibility, and chronic conditions. *Frontiers in Psychology, 11,* Article 1792. https://doi.org/10.3389/fpsyg.2020.01792

Porges, S. W. (2011). *The polyvagal theory: Neurophysiological foundations of emotions, attachment, communication, and self-regulation.* W. W. Norton.

Porges, S. W. (2017). Vagal pathways: Portals to compassion. In E. M. Seppälä, E. Simon-Thomas, S. L. Brown, M. C. Worline, C. D. Cameron, & J. R. Doty (Eds.), *The Oxford handbook of compassion science* (pp. 189–204). Oxford University Press.

Porges, S. W., & Lewis, G. F. (2010). The polyvagal hypothesis: Common mechanisms mediating autonomic regulation, vocalizations and listening. In S. M. Bruzynski (Ed.), *Handbook of mammalian vocalization: An integrative neuroscience approach* (pp. 255–264). Academic Press.

Price, C. J., & Hooven, C. (2018). Interoceptive awareness skills for emotion regulation: Theory and approach of mindful awareness in body-oriented therapy (MABT). *Frontiers in Psychology, 9,* Article 798. https://doi.org/10.3389/fpsyg.2018.00798

Raffone, A., Tagini, A., & Srinivasan, N. (2010). Mindfulness and the cognitive neuroscience of attention and awareness. *Zygon, 45*(3), 627–646. https://doi.org/10.1111/j.1467-9744.2010.01118.x

Razmjou, E., Freeman, H., Vladagina, N., Freitas, J., & Brems, C. (2017). Popular media images of yoga: Limiting perceived access to a beneficial practice. *Media Psychology Review, 11*(2). https://mprcenter.org/review/popular-media-images-of-yoga-limiting-perceived-access-to-a-beneficial-practice/

Reik, T. (1983). *Listening with the third ear.* Macmillan.

Rhodes, A., Spinazzola, J., & van der Kolk, B. (2016). Yoga for adult women with chronic PTSD: A long-term follow-up study. *The Journal of Alternative and Complementary Medicine, 22*(3), 189–196. https://doi.org/10.1089/acm.2014.0407

Riskind, J. H., & Gotay, C. C. (1982). Physical posture: Could it have regulatory or feedback effects on motivation and emotion? *Motivation and Emotion, 6*(3), 273–298. https://psycnet.apa.org/doi/10.1007/BF00992249

Rosenberg, S. (2017). *Accessing the healing power of the vagus nerve: Self-help exercises for anxiety, depression, trauma, and autism.* North Atlantic Books.

Rothschild, B. (2010). *8 keys to safe trauma recovery: Take-charge strategies to empower your healing.* W. W. Norton.

Ruden, R. A. (2011). *When the past is always present: Emotional traumatization, causes, and cures.* Routledge.

Saoji, A. A., Raghavendra, B. R., & Manjunath, N. K. (2019). Effects of yogic breath regulation: A narrative review of scientific evidence. *Journal of Ayurveda and Integrative Medicine, 10*(1), 50–58. https://doi.org/10.1016/j.jaim.2017.07.008

Scaer, R. (2014). *The body bears the burden: Trauma, dissociation, and disease* (3rd ed.). Routledge.

Schleip, R. (2017). Fascia as a sensory organ. In T. Liem, P. Tozzi, & A. Chila (Eds.), *Fascia in the osteopathic field* (pp. 137–163). Handspring Publishing.

Schwartz, R. C. (1997). *Internal family systems therapy.* Guilford Press.

Seoane, K. J. (2016). Parenting the self with self-applied touch: A dance/movement therapy approach to self-regulation. *American Journal of Dance Therapy, 38*(1), 21–40. https://doi.org/10.1007/s10465-016-9207-3

Seppälä, E. M., Nitschke, J. B., Tudorascu, D. L., Hayes, A., Goldstein, M. R., Nguyen, D. T. H., Perlman, D., & Davidson, R. J. (2014). Breathing-based meditation decreases posttraumatic stress disorder symptoms in U.S. military veterans: A randomized controlled longitudinal study. *Journal of Traumatic Stress, 27*(4), 397–405. https://doi.org/10.1002/jts.21936

Shaffer, F., McCraty, R., & Zerr, C. L. (2014). A healthy heart is not a metronome: An integrative review of the heart's anatomy and heart rate variability. *Frontiers in Psychology, 5*, Article 1040. https://doi.org/10.3389/fpsyg.2014.01040

Shapiro, F. (2018). *Eye movement desensitization and reprocessing (EMDR) therapy: Basic principles, protocols, and procedures* (3rd ed.). Guilford Press.

Sharma, V. K., Trakroo, M., Subramaniam, V., Rajajeyakumar, M., Bhavanani, A. B., & Sahai, A. (2013). Effect of fast and slow pranayama on perceived stress and cardiovascular parameters in young health-care students. *International Journal of Yoga, 6*(2), 104–110. https://doi.org/10.4103/0973-6131.113400

Shetty, P., Reddy, B. K. K., Lakshmeesha, D. R., Shetty, S. P., Kumar, G. S., & Bradley, R. (2017). Effects of Sheetali and Sheetkari pranayamas on blood pressure and autonomic function in hypertensive patients. *Integrative Medicine: A Clinician's Journal, 16*(5), 32–37. https://www.ncbi.nlm.nih.gov/pmc/articles/PMC6438091/pdf/imcj-16-32.pdf

Siegel, D. J. (1999). *The developing mind: How relationships and the brain interact to shape who we are.* Guilford Press.

Stickgold, R. (2002). EMDR: A putative neurobiological mechanism of action. *Journal of Clinical Psychology, 58*(1), 61–75. https://doi.org/10.1002/jclp.1129

Sullivan, M. B., Erb, M., Schmalzl, L., Moonaz, S., Noggle Taylor, J., & Porges, S. W. (2018). Yoga therapy and polyvagal theory: The convergence of traditional wisdom and contemporary neuroscience for self-regulation and resilience. *Frontiers in Human Neuroscience, 12*, Article 67. https://doi.org/10.3389/fnhum.2018.00067

Suveg, C., Braunstein West, K., Davis, M., Caughy, M., Smith, E. P., & Oshri, A. (2019). Symptoms and synchrony: Mother and child internalizing problems moderate respiratory sinus arrhythmia concordance in mother–preadolescent dyads. *Developmental Psychology, 55*(2), 366–376. https://doi.org/10.1037/dev0000648

Tanaka, S. (2015). Intercorporeality as a theory of social cognition. *Theory and Psychology, 25*(4), 455–472. https://doi.org/10.1177%2F0959354315583035

Tang, Y.-Y., Hölzel, B. K., & Posner, M. I. (2015). The neuroscience of mindfulness meditation. *Nature Reviews Neuroscience, 16*(4), 213–225. https://doi.org/10.1038/nrn3916

Teicher, M. H., & Samson, J. A. (2016). Annual research review: Enduring neurobiological effects of childhood abuse and neglect. *Journal of Child Psychology and Psychiatry, 57*(3), 241–266. https://dx.doi.org/10.1111%2Fjcpp.12507

Telles, S., Singh, N., & Balkrishna, A. (2011). Heart rate variability changes during high frequency yoga breathing and breath awareness. *BioPsychoSocial Medicine, 5*(1), Article 4. https://doi.org/10.1186/1751-0759-5-4

Thandi, G., Tom, D., Gould, M., McKenna, P., & Greenberg, N. (2015). Impact of a single-session of havening. *Health Science Journal, 9*(5), 1–5. https://www.hsj.gr/medicine/impact-of-a-singlesession-of-havening.pdf

Toussaint, L. L., Worthington, E. L., Jr., & Williams, D. R. (Eds.). (2015). *Forgiveness and health: Scientific evidence and theories relating forgiveness to better health.* Springer.

Trakroo, M., & Bhavanani, A. B. (2016). Physiological benefits of yogic practices: A brief review. *International Journal of Traditional and Complementary Medicine, 1*(1), 0031–0043. https://escipub.com/Articles/IJTCM/Vol1/Trakroo-IJTCM-2016

Tyagi, A., & Cohen, M. (2016). Yoga and heart rate variability: A comprehensive review of the literature. *International Journal of Yoga, 9*(2), 97–113. https://dx.doi.org/10.4103%2F0973-6131.183712

van der Kolk, B. A. (2006). Clinical implications of neuroscience research in PTSD. *Annals of the New York Academy of Sciences, 1071*(1), 277–293. https://doi.org/10.1196/annals.1364.022

van der Kolk, B. A., Stone, L., West, J., Rhodes, A., Emerson, D., Suvak, M., & Spinazzola, J. (2014). Yoga as an adjunctive treatment for posttraumatic stress disorder: A randomized controlled trial. *Journal of Clinical Psychiatry, 75*(6), e559–e565. https://doi.org/10.4088/jcp.13m08561

Wang, S.-Z., Li, S., Xu, X.-Y., Lin, G.-P., Shao, L., Zhao, Y., & Wang, T. H. (2010). Effect of slow abdominal breathing combined with biofeedback on blood pressure and heart rate variability in prehypertension. *The Journal of Alternative and Complementary Medicine, 16*(10), 1039–1045. https://doi.org/10.1089/acm.2009.0577

Wolynn, M. (2016). *It didn't start with you: How inherited family trauma shapes who we are and how to end the cycle.* Viking Press.

Yilmaz Balban, M., Cafaro, E., Saue-Fletcher, L., Washington, M. J., Bijanzadeh, M., Lee, A. M., Chang, E. F., & Huberman, A. D. (2021). Human responses to visually evoked threat. *Current Biology, 31*(3), 601–612. https://doi.org/10.1016/j.cub.2020.11.035

Zaccaro, A., Piarulli, A., Laurino, M., Garbella, E., Menicucci, D., Neri, B., & Gemignani, A. (2018). How breath-control can change your life: A systematic review on psycho-physiological correlates of slow breathing. *Frontiers in Human Neuroscience, 12*, Article 353. https://doi.org/10.3389/fnhum.2018.00353